What others are saying about this work:

"Susan helped me do things better…learn to spell, ride my bike, run faster and not be afraid to dive in the deep end of the pool. And reading is more fun." –Jack Dailey, 7, Indiana

"When Walt saw you, he was unable to apply pencil to paper or do math. He now writes very well and he has applied what you opened for him towards math. He has memorized his times tables and can multiply and divide. … He's been 100 percent mainstreamed from Special Ed. He now loves school and has friends at home, school, and church. Thanks for your help." –Barbara H., Victorville, California

"Lauren is starting to see for herself some of the wonderful positive effects of our visit to you. Her math tutor says she is far more focused and much more readily grasps concepts that before were difficult. Lauren herself says it is a real treat to read her history text—once— and understand what she read—and remember what she read!! She feels very happy … in control … and not in angst at all about final exams which start this week." –Jean S., Barrier, Ontario

"I was able to sit in a meeting all day without fidgeting, normally I would only last an hour" –Doug R., 53, Concord, New Hampshire

Taylor's time spent doing those two math pages has gone from three hours to one hour. Life in our household has been so happy. His attitude is very positive and tasks get done quickly and correctly. He loves to do things that make me cry with happiness. Tomorrow is a big test as it will be the first day back at school. And Tay is going to go Ritalin-free!! He is really easy to live with now and doesn't get into everything like he used to. Our life has changed so much in such a short time. Thank you, thank you, thank you! –Sherri M., Richmond, B.C.

Before treatment Amber says she was "in a cloud": "I was really lost. I had to be told over and over again what to do, and I would forget. [Now] I'm able to do everything. I can drive. I can read better. I can do

my math, go on errands and remember things." –Amber K.,
Longmont, Colorado

Three months later, after she'd resumed school in the fall, her first report card arrived. Jenna received 7 straight As –even math and history, 1 A plus in geography and 2 Bs, up from Bs, Cs, and a few As last year. –Jenna R., Toronto

Maxine was in her forties when I treated her for memory loss after a car accident. She had suffered disorientation and the loss of her extraordinary photographic memory following the accident. Recalling simple facts, such as the current president or the day of the week, became impossible. Making a shopping list or adding numbers was not manageable. And slowing down her car was no longer an automatic reflex. Instead, she had to remember how to lift her foot, press it on the pedal, and lift it off. Occupational and physical therapies hadn't helped. After the first session of BIT treatment, Maxine noticed a difference. She completed ten sessions and regained her ability to learn and to function. She went on to complete a degree in computer information systems. –Maxine K., Longmont, Colorado

"This is such a miracle that it's almost like my job is to tell people of its existence. . . . Thank you for changing my children's destiny. I will forever be grateful." –parents of Peter and Christopher R., West Vancouver, B.C.

"Sue is an articulate and persuasive spokesperson for the Learning Disabilities community. Like many of the best clinicians in the field, she struggled with learning problems that prevented her from excelling in school." –Mike Gismondi, LPC, New York

"Brain integration is the key to enabling people to be adaptable in an ever-changing world." –A. Schatz, Germany

Learning Difficulties in the U.S.:

The U.S. National Institute of Health say that fifteen percent of Americans have learning difficulties.

According to a 1987 study, Substance Abuse and Psychopathology, by P. A. Harrison and N. G. Hoffmann, 5.27 percent of the total student population in their study had a learning difficulty but 18.6 percent of students who had completed treatment for *chemical dependency* had a learning difficulty. This suggests that learning difficulties can lead to such stress in teens' lives that they turn to drugs and alcohol as a coping mechanism.

Another study by the U.S. Department of Education Office of Educational Research and Improvement in 1990 showed that children with early anti-social behavior and ADHD are at greater risk for teenage drug use and dependence.

Breaking
the Learning Barrier

Breaking
the Learning Barrier

Eradicating ADD, ADHD,
and Dyslexia

Susan McCrossin, A.P.

"Using case studies and jargon-free language,
McCrossin describes how she has been
transforming brains and lives since 1988."

—Mike Gismondi, LPC, Licensed Psychotherapist

Invaluable assistance from: Amy Thornbury

Illustrations: Kriss Wittmann and Rick Brunson

Copy Editing: Jody Berman and Joan Sherman

Design: ampersand graphic design, inc.

Photography: Garrett Hacking, www.photographyg.com

For information contact:

www.crossinology.com

ISBN 0-9761096-0-3

First printing October 2004

Published by Learning Enhancement Center LLC

This book is dedicated to all children and adults who are looking for a drug-free alternative for treating ADD, ADHD, or dyslexia that will remove their learning difficulties and enable them to live successful, productive lives.

Contents

Foreword 1

Preface 5

Introduction 9
   Did you find school difficult? .9
   What Is Brain Integration Technique (BIT)? 11
   Real-Life Stories of BIT Results 12

Chapter One: How the Brain Works and the
Origins of Learning Difficulties 23
   Our Brains Are Designed to Work Efficiently 25
   A Father-Son Story 26
   Conventional Understanding 28
   An Updated Model 29
   Two Hemispheres 31
   Full Integration 34

Chapter Two: How to Tell If There's
Dysfunction in the Brain 37
   What to Look For: Immaturity, Unusual Locomotion,
   or Lack of Coordination 38
   Avoiding Difficult, Stressful Tasks 42
   Living a Medicine-Free, Attention-Deficit-Free Life 48
   Self-Motivation 49
   Major Patterns of Specific Learning Difficulties 50
      Gestalt Dominance (or ADD) .50
      Logic Dominance (or dyslexia) 54
      Limited Access to Both Gestalt and Logic Functions 55
      Poor Integration of Gestalt and Logic Functions 56

Chapter Three: How Muscle Testing and
Applied Physiology Developed .59
   The Origins of Muscle Testing .59

The Introduction of Kinesiology
by R. W. Lovett (1932) 59
Academic Kinesiology and the Work of
Henry and Florence Kendall, George Goodheart,
and Frank Chapman (1930s and 1940s) 60
Terence Bennett's Work on Blood Flow (1930s) 61
Applied Kinesiology 61
East and West Combine: Goodheart's Work
in the 1960s 61
Richard Utt and the International
Institute of Applied Physiology 62
How Can Muscle Testing Tell You Anything? 64

Chapter Four: Understanding Crossinology's BIT 67
The Origins of Crossinology's
Brain Integration Technique 67
The Nature of Specific Learning Difficulties 68
Standard Psychological Tests Show Which Brain
Functions Are Having Difficulty 70
Crossinology's Brain Integration Technique
Restores Brain Functions 72
How Brain Integration Works 72
Traumas Early in Life 73
More on Muscle Testing 74
A Typical Course of Treatment 77
The Gift of Normalized Brain Function:
    Real-Life Stories 80
    Self-Confidence Soars 82
    Organic Brain Damage 84

Chapter Five: What the Future Holds 89

**Appendix A: Behavioral Checklist
for Learning Difficulties 95**

Appendix B:

Research Supporting Clinical Observations **97**

    Steady State Visual Evoked Potential

    Topography Changes 97

    Measuring BIT's Effects on Children with

    Learning Difficulties 103

Acronyms 110

Recommended Reading 111

Quick Order Form 113

Foreword

American families are witnessing a crisis in the way some children are experiencing school and struggling with taking their place in adult society. Regardless of what we call the problem—ADD, ADHD, hyperactivity, dyslexia, conduct disorders, learning difficulties, or simply underachievement and underemployment—there is no real consensus about how to treat the problem or even understand why so many of our children and young adults (as much as 15 percent of the entire U.S. population) cannot achieve success in school or perform in the work world. In fact, as society becomes more violent, less productive, and more prone to drug and alcohol abuse, the search for answers becomes that much more urgent.

To complicate matters, traditional Western medicine relies heavily on the use of medication, especially stimulants such as Ritalin, to address the crisis at hand. Stimulants have a desirable therapeutic effect less than 65 percent of the time, and even then, research has shown stimulants merely reduce some agitation or provide a little more mental stamina during the day. But grades generally don't improve; memory, attention, and planning deficits persist; and the goal of achieving academic and vocational excellence remains as distant as before. Finally, the worrisome side effects and long-term impact of stimulants on a developing brain make the "overprescribing" issue a very real concern.

However, the advent of complementary medicine offers hope for those afflicted with learning difficulties. Perhaps one of the most powerful and promising new approaches comes from the world of kinesiology and acupressure (also known as needle-less acupuncture). In the 1980s, a number of inventive healers around the world combined knowledge about how the brain learns with the ancient wisdom of Chinese medicine. Out of this body of work came "miracles": people with long-standing learning difficulties, head injuries, and even strokes recovered in dramatic ways. One of the most innovative and gifted of those healers is Susan McCrossin, a native of Australia who is trained in Chinese acupressure and kinesiology along with the rapidly expanding fields of neuroscience and applied cognitive psychology.

At the heart of McCrossin's treatment system are two interlocking concepts of neurology and acupressure. Neuroscience, as exemplified by the work of Antonio Damasio, M.D., has stressed that the key to brain organization and performance is "time binding," that is, the coordination and the synchronization of many separate activities in different parts of the brain that permits the successful performance of mental skills such as memorization, planning, or testing a solution to a novel problem. During normal development, the brain's communication and coordination systems grow in a hierarchical manner, whereby we first master basic sensory-motor tasks and later learn how to coordinate our emotions and higher-order cognitive skills. This finely tuned hierarchical coordination is vulnerable to disruption via emotional stress in the amygdala, the brain's alarm system. The amygdala has the dual task of "remembering" and alerting us to possible emotional/physical threats attaching enough meaning and order to new material to make it memorable and retrievable when needed. Unfortunately, certain types of emotional stress, especially early in life when the brain is still developing, can cause the amygdala to confuse real and imagined danger and make these alarm processes so readily triggered that normal learning is compromised. Crossinology's Brain Integration Technique (BIT), developed by McCrossin, releases these "hyperactive" emotional stress circuits and reinstates the brain's normal information-processing and problem-solving machinery. Research indicates that changes in blood flow and brain-wave patterns resulting from the technique are directed to certain parts of the brain and allow their intended functions to "wake up" and override the alarm circuits that prevented optimal learning in the past.

The goal of this book is to share with parents and the general public the excitement and hope of these new, non-drug-based approaches to the rapid treatment of learning problems. Using case studies and jargon-free language, McCrossin describes how she has been transforming brains and lives since 1988.

—Mike Gismondi, LPC, Licensed Psychotherapist

Preface

Through many years of working with children and adults who have dyslexia, ADD, ADHD, and a host of other learning difficulties, I am compelled to share what I have seen with as wide an audience as possible. Recent developments have made it possible to permanently eradicate these difficulties with as little as eight to twelve hours of noninvasive, drug-free treatment.

In my own experience with a learning difficulty, I found myself slipping through the cracks of the Australian school system as a teenager. I thought I was condemned to a life without academic success because of an undiagnosed learning problem. Years later, after leaving a thriving career in the computer industry, I discovered that techniques developed in applied physiology, a form of kinesiology (also known as muscle testing), could be combined with related techniques and used to correct learning difficulties in children and adults.

In talking with parents and youngsters who had learning difficulties, I realized their experiences mirrored my own frustration during my school years; in fact, I realized that I had a form of dyslexia stemming from a lack of visual memory, that is, "seeing in the mind's eye" function that is needed for storing information. After I received treatment for my own inabilities, I was suddenly able to succeed in academics as never before.

I enrolled in Melbourne's Swinburne University and received dual advanced degrees in neuroscience and psychology. My grades were surprisingly good, enabling me to qualify for an additional year of honors research, which I used to conduct state-of-the-art EEG brain research into the techniques that I had used on others and on myself to wipe out learning deficits. The studies showed a normalization of brain-wave patterns in all the subjects who received treatment.

These techniques have become the basis for an eighty-step process called the Brain Integration Technique, or BIT, which was developed at my center in Melbourne in 1988 and brought by me to Boulder, Colorado, ten years later to serve a wider audience. My motivation for writing this book is to bring this revolutionary form of treatment to an even broader spectrum of the world's population in hopes that it will offer the kind of life-changing, consciousness-raising experience to others, just as it did to me.

BIT grew out of an overall philosophy that I call Crossinology®. It is a therapeutic model that helps people with learning difficulties, allergies, closed-head injuries, limitations from a stroke or head trauma, and sports injuries involving muscles and joints. Results include improved creativity, greater learning ability, enhanced behavioral attitudes, and better physical coordination.

Crossinology is also an interrelated approach bringing together all the energetic healing methods that connect into an individual's mind and body in order to optimize function in any area. The essence of Crossinology is to help us reach our full potential and to pursue our true passions by having a fully functional brain.

Like all complex network systems, the body and mind are linked with a deep underlying order and operate according to simple but powerful rules. The road from disorder to order is maintained by powerful forces of self-organization, and when given the chance, the body and mind will "renormalize" themselves. This order within networks allows for a resynchronization in the brain when appropriate opportunities are provided. Crossinology's BIT is one of these opportunities.

BIT is not a tutoring or training method. It is a therapeutic treatment focused on eradicating learning difficulties through renormalizing brain pathways.

It's been reported that since 2001, the use of drugs (such as Ritalin) for treating attention deficit disorders in children under age five has risen a dramatic 49 percent.[1] Estimates vary, but from 3 to 10 percent of all children have attention deficit problems, and 20 percent suffer from learning difficulties such as dyslexia and dyspraxia. Clearly, the need for alternative treatment is great.

---

[1] Linda A. Johnson, "Spending Soars for Kids' Behavior Drugs," *Washington Post*, May 17, 2004.

To help you determine if you, your child, or your spouse, friend or other loved one has a learning difficulty, I've provided a checklist at the back of this book (see Appendix A). Keep in mind that, although many of us exhibit some of the behaviors on the list from time to time, the person with a learning difficulty exhibits many of the symptoms all of the time. As a parent, it can be scary and frustrating to be confronted with something such as dyslexia or ADD and the associated perplexing behaviors in a child. And adults, too, can have undiagnosed learning difficulties—problems that often result in a lifetime of struggles, crises at work, tension in families, and difficult social lives.

Though you may be feeling you're in over your head, my message is to assure you that there is hope, instead of despair; there is calm, instead of fear; and there is correction, instead of compensation.

The treatment described in this book—BIT—is designed not only to improve academic success through the ability to be a more efficient learner but also to develop better relationships with friends and family. BIT can help to remove the stumbling blocks that stand in the way of true happiness. Treatment can enhance mental and even physical health by eliminating mental stress. Best of all, the sooner treatment is received, the sooner you or your loved one can begin living life to its fullest potential, no longer burdened by subconscious impediments. Ultimately, I hope to use this treatment to allow you and those you love to be all that you were meant to be.

…when the brain is
not integrated, learning and life
become more difficult … as if
you're not firing on all cylinders.

Introduction

Did you find school difficult? Do you see your children struggling to memorize, comprehend, and perform well on tests? Do you notice a gap between what you know and what you do?

The brain is the interface between the body, mind, and spirit. When your brain is integrated—meaning that all of its parts are connected and functioning in an organized manner—you're able to cope easily with all aspects of life. An integrated brain enables you to live a full life with the  ability to develop your potential. But when the brain is not integrated, learning and life become more difficult, and there is the constant sensation that you're not performing up to your potential, as if you're not firing on all cylinders.

Through normal yet stressful life experiences, the brain often develops inefficient ways to process information. These stresses occur early in life, typically between birth and five years of age. It can be traumatic, for instance, for a young child if their primary caregiver becomes very ill, for the child's very survival depends on this person. Or the stress could come from the birth of a sibling, especially if the older child is under two years of age. From the first child's perspective, having been the center of the universe with their parents' complete attention, it's very stressful when a tiny newborn is suddenly taking much of that attention away. Not all children react to these events by shutting down part of their brain processing, but some do and they do it as a coping strategy to avoid some of the emotional pain of the situations they confront. Of course, they don't realize they are doing so or that they are going to need those parts of the brain for academic performance in the years ahead. By the time they start school, the original stress is long forgotten, and so the connection between the original stress and the subsequent learning difficulty is not even considered.

The impact of shutting down part of the brain's processing—what I call poor brain integration—is just as startling as the results that can be achieved from reintegration and restoration of brain circuitry through the Brain Integration Technique.

What Is Brain Integration Technique?

BIT helps people with learning difficulties (such as dyslexia, attention deficit disorder [ADD], and attention deficit/hyperactivity disorder [ADHD]) by correcting the misrouting and the improper timing of information being sent to the brain, clearing any blocks along the way and thereby breaking the barriers to learning. BIT therapy addresses concentration, memory, visual processing, auditory processing, planning, and comprehension. The time required for treatment varies from case to case, but typically, the corrections are completed in eight to twelve hours using a combination of acupressure and muscle testing, both of which are completely noninvasive procedures.

Acupressure is different from acupuncture in that it does not involve needles; only light pressure from the fingertips is applied in precise locations on the body. The technique is sometimes called "needle-less acupuncture." **Muscle testing** is a technique used to determine whether a muscle resists downward pressure. The noninvasive, nonpainful procedure involves checking whether the arm, for example, resists gentle downward pressure or collapses easily. If it resists, the muscle is said to test "strong"; if it collapses, the muscle tests "weak." In this way, muscle testing is used as a biofeedback tool and reveals whether specific pathways in the brain are blocked or unblocked. Together, acupressure and muscle testing allow the trained BIT practitioner to know which pathways need treatment to restore brain functions.

MRI (Magnetic resonance imaging) and SPECT, (Single-photon emission computed tomography) scans have shown that, compared with individuals with normal brain activity, people with learning difficulties have decreased blood flow in areas of the brain responsible for specific tasks such as reading.[2] When the blood flow is restored to those parts of the brain through acupressure, the learning difficulties are corrected and the brain behaves normally. BIT restores normal blood flow to information-processing and problem-solving circuitry in the brain. As a result, learning difficulties are either lessened or completely eliminated.

Real-Life Stories of BIT Results

Christopher

Christopher's father brought him to see me after hearing about Crossinology's Learning Enhancement Center in Boulder, Colorado, from a friend in Vancouver. I treated Christopher over three and a half days in August 2002 when he was thirteen and about to enter seventh grade.

Christopher had been having difficulty with schoolwork, especially math. "Tutoring wasn't helping," his father, David, said, "and we

---

2   Christine Gorman, "New Science of Dyslexia," *Time*, July 28, 2003. The article estimates that "up to one in five kids may simply not be 'wired' to read."

wanted to catch it as early as possible because math builds on itself." Christopher had never been able to memorize his multiplication tables, and he labored to multiply numbers by counting up to the number required. As he reached middle school, he encountered math problems that were more complicated, such as (3 x 8) - (10 ÷ 2). His father explained, "By the time he figured out that 3 x 8 = 24, he'd forgotten what the rest of the problem was."

Christopher had seen a psychologist in Canada who administered an IQ test, the Wechsler Intelligence Scale for Children—Third Edition Revised (WISC IIIR). This test is widely used in North America to gauge intellectual and cognitive abilities in children ages six to sixteen relative to their peers. The WISC has been used for more than sixty years because it has a high test-retest reliability; in other words, if you score in the fiftieth percentile of the population at age six, you'll score in the fiftieth percentile of the population when you're sixty. On a scale from 1 to 19, some of Christopher's scores were in the superior range, some were average, and some were below average, specifically his coding score (an 8) and his symbol search score (a 7), which put him at the twenty-first percentile of his age group for processing speed. Both of the tasks measured by these scores rely on visual short-term memory to be performed well. Further educational testing showed that Christopher was a fast reader but had poor comprehension unless allowed to read and reread. He was typical of many people with learning difficulties in that by his age, persistence had enabled him to be able to read (i.e., interpret the words on the page), but he didn't read for pleasure because it was still a struggle to comprehend *what* he read.

During his first treatment, a two-hour session with me, I used muscle testing—a form of biofeedback—to assess the degree to which Christopher could access various pathways in his brain. I found that he had very little access to the pathways in his corpus callosum, the fibers that connect the right and left halves of the brain. The corpus callosum works a bit like the old telephone switchboard, ensuring that connections take place between the two hemispheres (or sides) of the brain. Muscle testing revealed that half of Christopher's brain, the Gestalt side (often called the right brain, even though it isn't always actually located in the right side), was fully functioning. However, the other half, the half that is responsible for logic, had very little access to pathways responsible for visual construction (the ability to make pictures in the head, a skill used for spelling). He also had low access to the brain pathways that assign meaning to words for reading comprehension. As for the logic part of his brain, which is essential to math skills, Christopher had access to less than half of his capacity for arithmetic functions.

After eleven hours of sessions, I completed the BIT treatment, and Christopher now had total access to the pathways in all areas. As he

and his father left, I recommended that Christopher's parents do some "imprinting" work with flash cards to help load up Christopher's mind with the math facts he had previously been unable to master. The imprinting method has been around a long time; grandmothers in Australia have told me they used it when they were children. In a nutshell, the method involves having the child look at a flash card, say aloud what is on it, trace the information with his finger, and take a "picture" of the information by snapping his eyelids closed like the shutter of a camera. The child is then asked to recall the math fact (or word) one hour, twenty-four hours, and a week after learning it. If he recalls it successfully, the fact is in his memory for life. Once the flash card material has been mastered in this manner, it is his forever—a feat previously thought impossible for this child. But without opening access to the area of the brain that stores such information, the well-established flash card technique will not work, no matter how many repetitions are endured.

When they returned home, Christopher and his parents worked methodically during the final weeks of summer vacation to imprint facts with flash cards, and Christopher learned them. At last, he was able to memorize because he could finally make the mental pictures necessary for appropriate storage and retrieval.

About three months after treatment, in November 2002, the family was sitting at home on a Sunday afternoon when the phone rang. It was Christopher's homeroom teacher calling. David remembers the call vividly: "She said, 'I don't know what's happened. I just graded Christopher's math test. This was a tough exam; other kids didn't do as well. Christopher got a 92 percent!'

She was blown away by his progress, and it was only then that we told her about Christopher's treatment at your clinic."

By the end of that school year, his mother sent me an E-mail, saying, "Christopher brought home his latest math score yesterday. He scored 100%. Two weeks ago he scored 99%. This from a child who used to barely get 50%. His confidence is soaring. Thank you."

Above all, the change in Christopher's attitude toward school was evident. As his father said, "He's definitely not experiencing the level of frustration that he was experiencing previously. ... I think he's finding school a lot more enjoyable than it was before. ... He's had a huge improvement in math, which was exactly what we were looking for. Both my wife and I are absolutely satisfied that the treatment had a positive impact on his abilities at school."

Peter

Christopher's dramatic change prompted his parents to bring their older son, Peter, age fifteen, to me in March 2003. Peter had been diagnosed with a problem in sequentially processing information visually. This meant he had, among other things, difficulty in concentrating and in budgeting his time. He struggled to give or to remember directions. He had poor organizational skills and was slow to complete work. He couldn't spell well, and he frequently mispronounced words. Peter's WISC IIIR test scores ran the gamut, with superior abilities in verbal comprehension and writing fluency but a glaring deficit in processing speed that put him in the second percentile among North Americans his age. This score indicated "a severe learning difficulty in timed written motor output owing to difficulties with visual memory and visual sequencing," wrote the psychologist who administered the test.

Peter's initial testing with me, which involved muscle testing, indicated he had just 4 *percent* access to the areas responsible for visual construction (a function in the brain critical to spelling, among other tasks). He had full access to auditory construction (i.e., the ability to make images from what he heard for spelling or reading, making him a so-called auditory learner), but he had only 12 percent access to the areas that assign meaning to words, necessary for reading comprehension. Finally, he had less than 50 percent access to the areas responsible for mathematical functions (adding and subtracting).

I treated Peter over the course of three days, and when we were finished, all of his brain processing areas were shown through muscle testing to be fully functional. When he returned home, he continued to work with his tutor, who had no idea that he had received the BIT treatment but commented that "his brain seems to be working better."

Six months after treatment, Peter demonstrated a new level of initiative that his father described as "remarkable, anecdotal proof" of the shift in the boy's attitude since receiving Crossinology's BIT treatment to restore brain functions. At Peter's school, there was a competitive program that challenged students to meet certain requirements in all areas of academics: "It's a prestigious program that few students are willing to pursue because it is so demanding," said David. "I was blown away when he announced he'd chosen to pursue the award. Whether he succeeds or not, he's going to attack it, and that's a big shift for him. Peter has developed a drive and level of responsibility that he never had before."

Since 2002, a dozen or so of the hundreds of people who have arrived at my clinic for treatment have come at David's urging. And he has asked them to report back to him about their experiences. "I've had nothing but positive feedback," he has reported. "One woman was practically in tears when she came back because her thirteen-year-old son had such immediate, positive results. That encouraged me to tell more people. This is such a miracle that it's almost like my job is to tell people of its existence." Peter and Christopher's mother wrote to me, as well: "Thank you for changing my children's destiny. I will forever be grateful."

> "Thank you for changing my children's destiny. I will forever be grateful."

Walt

Perhaps nowhere are the results of Brain Integration Technique more pronounced than in the case of students who, after treatment, no longer need to be placed in special-education classes. The following story illustrates the impact of such a shift.

Walt came to me in January 1999. He was eleven years old and a special-education student in the fifth grade. He had excellent scores in reading and oral work but unsatisfactory grades in writing and math. He often stuttered and became tongue-tied, and he especially had trouble concentrating and telling time. He also struggled with remembering times tables, following directions, turning in work, and taking any kind of test. The list of problems went on and included clumsiness, lack of coordination, dizziness, eyestrain, headaches, impatience and impulsivity, lack of confidence, and letter and number reversal. Walt also habitually told lies and had mood swings. Finally, he was poor at sports and rhythmic activities. His brain pathways were so disorganized that even a simple task would leave him exhausted, making him appear lethargic, inappropriately drowsy, and underactive.

Muscle testing of the corpus callosum showed Walt's "telephone exchange center" was working fine. His problem instead involved deep-level switching. These pathways were crossed, meaning that the right- and left-brain functions were confused, so the right brain thought it should handle left-brain functions and vice versa.

Picture the two halves of the brain, right and left, and a bit of information coming in for processing. If the information involves arithmetic, for example, it should initially be processed in the left half. But people with deep-level switching go through very inefficient processing, completely subconsciously and entirely beyond their own control. Incoming information actually enters the right half, is shunted over to the left half for processing, returned to the right half, and then shunted back out again. If the corpus callosum between the two hemispheres is blocked, information is dropped every time it passes through. When this occurs and the information is shunted out, or released, verbally, the individual can appear delayed in his response and somewhat slow mentally. Add some stress and the whole process starts to completely fall apart, with the tongue becoming tied in knots.

In a normal connection, information would go from point A to point B. But when neurocircuitry problems exist, information goes from A to C to D or E before reaching B. No wonder Walt was exhausted all the time! These neurocircuitry problems underlie a number of learning difficulties and behavior disorders, such as autism, Fragile X Syndrome, Pervasive Developmental Disorder (PDD), and a range of associated problems.

I treated Walt for a total of five hours over a few weeks. Once his pathways were uncrossed (in a functional, not a physical, sense), the brain was reintegrated and ready to learn. One month after treatment, Walt's math grades went from unsatisfactory to straight As. He was finishing his schoolwork now and had become more kind and affectionate. By April, he'd had a huge improvement in social skills and was making lots of friends. In June, he reported that his schoolwork was easier, he was handing in all of his assignments, and his teacher was impressed with his positive attitude.

The sense of relief and satisfaction felt by mother and son was nearly palpable. His mother sent me a thank-you note in December 1999 to say that Walt was now an honor-roll student and, furthermore, had won an award at his elementary school for his outstanding reading skills. "When Walt saw you, he was unable to apply pencil to paper or do math. He now writes very well and he has applied what you opened for him towards math. He has memorized his times tables and can multiply and divide. ...He's been 100 percent mainstreamed from Special Ed. He now loves school and has friends at home, school, and church. Thanks for your help."

Lauren

When I met Lauren in April 2003, she was fifteen years old. A competitive figure skater, she was quite sociable and had many friends at school, but she had suffered from very poor reading comprehension and difficulty expressing herself verbally throughout her school years. Test and performance anxiety were big problems, too. She had trouble with math, especially memorizing her times tables, and she scored at a fourth-grade equivalency for mathematics, reasoning and numerical operations on a WISC IIIR assessment. The assessment placed her vocabulary at the fifth percentile and her comprehension at the thirty-seventh percentile, roughly at a third- or fourth-grade level. Her processing speed scores, however, were quite good, placing her at the ninety-seventh percentile, and she had good auditory memory. A psychologist who tested Lauren described her as having "a mild language disorder which ... encompasses problems with expressing word meanings and concept formations as well as the misapplication of grammatical rules and syntax and relatively poor language comprehension." Upon initial assessment, I found Lauren needed correction to sort out the confusion about which side of her brain performed logic functions and which side performed creative, or Gestalt, functions; the messages being sent were all crossed. She had very low (4 percent) access to pathways in the corpus callosum. Her Gestalt hemisphere, testing at 100 percent access, was dominant over her logic hemisphere, which could access just 64 percent overall. She had only 7 percent access to pathways dealing with reading comprehension and 8 percent access to arithmetic functions. After treatment, these pathways were restored to 100 percent access.

Lauren's case illustrates the impact that brain integration has on overall well-being. When Lauren returned home, one of the first things she did was take a driving test for her learner's permit. She read the rules-of-the-road book without any help and passed the test with only three mistakes. She was especially pleased because a number of the items on the test were multiple-choice questions, a format she had struggled with previously. About a month after treatment, her mom wrote to me, "Lauren is starting to see for herself some of the wonderful positive effects of our visit to you. Her math tutor says she is far more focused and much more readily grasps concepts that before were difficult. Lauren herself says it is a real treat to read her history text—once—and understand what she read—and remember what she read!! She feels very happy … in control … and not in angst at all about final exams which start this week." This from a girl who previously suffered significant test anxiety!

When information enters the
brain, it needs to go to the
correct location with the proper
timing. When this doesn't
happen, we aren't able
to think or learn easily.

Chapter One

*How the Brain Works and the
Origins of Learning Difficulties*

Our brains are designed to integrate and process information like an orchestra performing a symphony. All the sections of the orchestra—the strings, brass, percussion, and woodwinds—are playing the same tune at the same time, creating a beautiful, harmonic sound.

When the sections of the orchestra are not playing in time with each other and when individual members within a section are not even playing the same piece of music, we get a cacophonous mess. It is stressful to listen to and stressful to participate in.

This disharmonious illustration is a metaphor for how the brain functions when learning difficulties are present. There is no harmony, and the timing is off. Someone with mild learning difficulties could have certain sections of the orchestra—the woodwinds, percussion, or strings—playing different pieces of music, whereas someone with profound learning difficulties could have every instrument playing a different piece, neither in time nor in harmony with anyone else.

Most of what we learn comes into our brains through our eyes and ears. When information enters the brain, it needs to go to the correct location with the proper timing. When this doesn't happen, we aren't able to think or learn easily.

Water flowing downhill will always take the easiest and most direct route. However, when it is blocked by a rock or other obstacle, the water will deviate around the barrier and then continue on its way. When there are a number of blockages, the water will still deviate around them, but each deviation will lengthen the time it takes the water to flow downhill and increase both the evaporation and the amount of water absorbed into the soil. Similarly, when blockages exist in the brain's processing, information not only takes longer to process but some of it also "evaporates" along the way. When the blockages are cleared in the brain, information is able to transfer quickly and easily to auditory short-term memory, then to visual short-term memory, and finally to visual long-term memory without any stress or effort at all. Learning is smooth and effortless.

Our Brains Are Designed to Work Efficiently

Our brains are built to learn. And learning is easy when all areas of the brain are accessible and all the routes that connect them are totally clear.

Our brains are designed to work efficiently, using both cerebral hemispheres and proper timing of brain signals.

Learning difficulties result from blockage to one or more subconscious functions in the brain. More severe learning difficulties are caused when there are several blocks to specific functions *and* blocks to the routes of integration.

I cannot stress enough that learning difficulties are a functional problem of the brain's circuitry and have nothing to do with intelligence or intelligence quotient (IQ) scores. Indeed, many bright people are not aware they have ADD or dyslexia until they are adults and the problem is diagnosed in their children. Learning difficulties were not well understood and frequently went undiagnosed or misdiagnosed during their own childhoods. But when they hear their children's difficulties described, they realize that the description matches their own experience.

A Father-Son Story

Consider the following father-son case. Thomas was a senior at the University of New Hampshire when he came to me for treatment in January of 2003. Diagnosed with ADD when he was very young, he found it impossible to concentrate on a conversation with another person if the television was on, for example. Before treatment, he said, "My concentration can become out of focus to the point where I cannot hear another person conversing with me." After having his brain circuitry renormalized, he was able to focus; his concentration greatly improved.

While Thomas was receiving treatment, his father, Doug, decided he would like to be treated as well. Doug, in his early fifties, also had ADD, and although he was a successful businessman, he had never been able to pay attention in meetings or classroom situations. Not only did he exhibit "classic ADD" symptoms (such as a poor ability to concentrate, pay attention, or budget his time), he also struggled to focus his eyes or follow directions.

After I treated Doug, an amazing thing happened. When his wife asked him how an all-day conference he'd attended had gone, he suddenly realized that instead of getting fidgety after an hour, as he always had previously, he'd been able to sit calmly all day and not even notice that he was doing so. *This sort of reaction is normal.* Until his wife asked, he hadn't been aware of the change. Just like we forget pain when we are no longer experiencing it, once Doug was free of the lifelong ADD that had plagued him, he forgot how difficult sitting still used to be because it now seemed normal.

As the preceding example illustrates, learning difficulties tend to run in families, which, according to current scientific belief, is thought to mean they are genetic. However, when I change someone's brain function, I don't believe I am changing his or her genetics. My theory—based on muscle testing thousands of clients—is that what is actually inherited is the emotional tendency to shut down part of the brain's functions if we are stressed at some point between birth and five years of age. We are all subjected to various forms of stress as we grow up, stresses

> Learning difficulties run in families but are not genetic.

that cannot be avoided even in the most "ideal" of families. But people react differently to stressful events, and some shut down part of their brains' functions as an effective coping strategy. This means the individuals don't have to deal with the stressful events at a time when they are, in fact, too young to put any kind of objective perspective on the situation. After all, many people have endured severe physical, mental, or emotional stress, often repeatedly, and had no memory of it whatsoever. Stressful events during our early lives can't be avoided and actually make us the unique individuals that we grow up to be. They are a normal part of our growth and development.

In my own case, I eventually traced my stress event back to when I was a toddler and my father traveled to Poughkeepsie, New York, for training at the IBM headquarters there. I was eighteen months old when he left, and he was gone for six months. Without any way of understanding where he had gone or that he would come back again, I did what many children do: I left the world emotionally so as not to feel that kind of pain again. Subconsciously, a part of my brain shut down. Of course, I had no idea I would need access to that area of the brain for learning later on.

Recall the story of Walt in the Introduction, a boy who was able to leave special-education classes after he received BIT treatment. Muscle testing revealed that when he was seventeen months old, Walt suffered emotional stress. I don't know or need to know the details of his trauma. What his situation underscores, however, is my belief and my clinical experience that brain adaptations usually occur in response to a traumatic event before age five. The brain shuts down the memory of a trauma in order to cope and function in life; such a response is an effective coping mechanism. These adaptations cause neuronal pathways to become crossed at a functional, not a physical, level. Once the pathways are normalized, the proper avenues for learning are opened up and made available.

Conventional Understanding

According to the conventional understanding of the human brain, reasoning takes place in the cortex—the top part of the brain. The cortex is what separates us from animals: it is much larger in humans and gives us the ability to think abstractly. Conventional thinking suggests that the cortex dominates all other areas of the brain, controls the body and behavior and, in a nutshell, makes us human.

> The conventional understanding holds that brain functions are linear and hierarchical.

Traditional belief has asserted that the flow of neural impulses in the brain is linear and hierarchical, which means that one brain function follows the next like a train traveling on a track and that some functions dominate other functions, giving priority to the act of thinking over the act of feeling or "emoting."

We have also traditionally believed the physical and mental tasks of the brain are localized and segregated in discrete regions of the cortex, so specific tasks occur in specific locations within the cortex. This line of reasoning asserts that functions are isolated by region in the brain and do not interact much with other parts of the brain.

Conventionally, too, we have believed the limbic system, also known as the reptilian part of the brain, is the center of our "animal" emotions and that these emotions are controlled by the reasoning function of the cortex. Accordingly, we have thought that the superior human cortex controlled our basic urges and behavior.

An Updated Model

During the 1990s, Antonio Damasio, a leading American neurologist, developed an updated model for how the brain works. This model describes the brain as a center for processing multiple tasks in parallel, meaning at the same time, instead of in linear and sequential order.

> An updated model explains that brain functions are multiple, complex, and simultaneous.

Consider the complex process of reading and understanding what you've just read. When you read, you are interpreting the words on the page, accessing those words from a part of your memory where word recognition is stored, and activating another part of your brain where comprehension and meaning are stored. Reading comprehension demonstrates this updated model, since it involves processing multiple tasks simultaneously.

From this updated model, we understand that the brain processes information in an extremely complex manner. Specific functions are not localized in discrete areas but are distributed to several areas of the brain, and the timing and integration of these functions give us our thoughts and mental activity.

Damasio's book, *Descartes' Error* (1995), showed that the limbic system is much more important than originally believed and that our behavior is controlled far more often by our emotions than by our logic. Purchasing decisions, whether involving a car, clothes, or music, are predominantly made by our emotions and not by reason and logic. Further, as anyone who struggles with dieting can attest, what we choose to eat is usually based on emotions, not logic.

For this reason, the Brain Integration Technique addresses the blood flow involved in the emotional subconscious. It is especially important to revise the emotions that are attached to certain behaviors. For example, the thought of speaking in public may trigger the emotion of fear, reading aloud may be associated with shame, and so forth. These associations must be cleared from the subconscious so the individual can truly "get on with her life" and begin learning—and behaving—as she was meant to do.

Two Hemispheres

The brain has two separate halves, or hemispheres, often referred to as the "right brain" and "left brain" because of their anatomical distinctness and the differences in how they process information. These hemispheres are not completely separate, however, but are connected at the bottom of the fissure (or gap) between them by a structure called the corpus callosum.

> The brain is divided in two hemispheres, the Gestalt (right brain) and the logic (left brain).

The corpus callosum is estimated to have approximately 200 to 500 million nerve fibers running between the two hemispheres. Neurologically, as I noted earlier, it functions much like a telephone exchange that allows a two-way flow of communication between the hemispheres. Whenever the hemispheres are required to work together to produce an integrated function (for instance, in reading), that integration takes place in the corpus callosum.

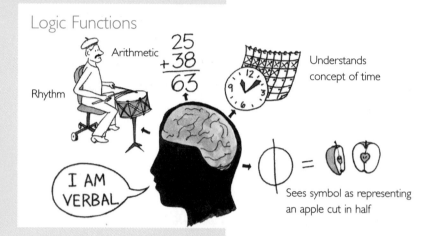

Each cerebral hemisphere initiates or carries out a number of discrete functions, and each handles information in a very different way from the other. It is as if each side of the brain has a special-

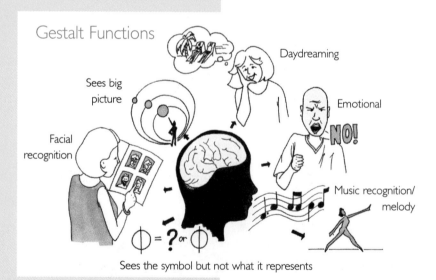

ized set of instructions, with the right hemisphere possessing a set of functions that complement those of the left hemisphere and vice versa. The functions in the left hemisphere in most people deal with the logically sequenced analysis of the parts of the whole.

Generally speaking, the functions that take place in the right hemisphere in most people are global, or Gestalt (meaning whole-picture or indivisible), and deal with the recognition of overall patterns. Thus, looking at a forest is a Gestalt, or right-brain, experience; studying and analyzing the trees is a logic, or left-brain, experience.

However, it is important to note that not all people have their Gestalt functions in the right half of the brain and their logic functions in the left half. In many people, the functions are reversed, with no impact on the brain's performance.

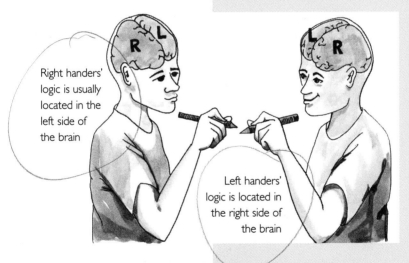

Right handers' logic is usually located in the left side of the brain

Left handers' logic is located in the right side of the brain

Left-handed, ambidextrous, and some right-handed people have "transposed hemispheres," wherein logic functions are located in the right hemisphere and Gestalt functions are in the left hemisphere. This is a normal variation in the population, and it has been noted there are both a higher number of geniuses and a greater incidence of learning difficulties within this population. People in this group often have superior abilities in seeing the overall picture, "intuiting" solutions, and being more tenacious, probably because they are used to overcoming setbacks. These traits give them the skills to be good entrepreneurs if they can overcome the negative impact of their school experiences and maintain good self-esteem.

Full Integration

Learning and thinking are not functions that occur only in the left or right side of the brain. Different learning tasks require access to many diverse functions and combinations of functions in the brain. Both hemispheres participate all the time and at many levels in the various thought processes. The way we think is a result of the degree of integration between the two hemispheres.

> Proper integration of the right and left hemispheres of the brain is necessary to process information efficiently and effectively.

Each hemisphere lends its own special capabilities to all cognitive activities. The contributions of each are clearly demonstrated during complex mental activities such as reading, as explained in the following excerpt from *Psychology Today*:

All areas of the brain open

When a person reads a story, the right hemisphere [Gestalt] may play a special role in decoding visual information, maintaining an integrated story structure, appreciating humor and emotional content, deriving meaning from past associations, and

understanding metaphor. At the same time, the left hemisphere [logic]
plays a special role in understanding syntax, translating written words
into their phonetic representations, and deriving meaning from complex
relationships among word concepts and syntax.[3]

Psychological and physiological evidence indicates that the relative
degree of work required in the two hemispheres varies depending
upon the nature of the tasks being performed. When doing simple
arithmetic tasks, such as counting
or adding one plus one, the
logic functions will be activated with little, if any, Gestalt
activity required. A predominantly Gestalt task, by contrast,
such as matching similar pat-
terns, will require little logic involvement. The more complex the
task becomes, the greater the degree of activation and integration
required in both hemispheres.

> Learning difficulties
> result from the inability
> to access specific brain
> functions or the inability
> to effectively integrate
> them.

Different learning tasks, therefore, require access to different
types of functions as well as varying coordination of these functions. Some of these functions are located predominantly in the
Gestalt/right brain; others are located predominantly in the
logic/left brain.

Complex learning tasks such as reading and spelling require
not only access to functions in both hemispheres but also the integration and simultaneous processing of information in both

---

3   J. Levy, "Right Brain, Left Brain: Fact and Fiction," *Psychology Today*, May 1985.

hemispheres. Therefore, if you can access all brain functions in both cerebral hemispheres with equal facility and can integrate these functions well, you will probably find learning easy.

However, if you cannot access certain brain functions or have difficulty integrating the functions for any reason, you may well have trouble performing tasks involving those specific functions. Tasks such as reading, spelling, doing higher-level mathematics, writing, organizing, memorizing, and sustaining attention over time are more complicated and rely on the proper integration of and access to brain functions. Deficiencies in some or all of these learning skills are the typical symptoms of ADD and dyslexia.

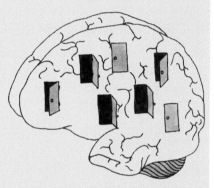

Limited access to all brain functions

Crossinology's Brain Integration Technique addresses any deficiencies by restoring the necessary integration and timing of brain functions. Treatment does not remove or change one's existing abilities; rather, it establishes connections that were previously disconnected and restores access to the functional areas of the brain. Tasks that were previously considered extremely difficult, if not impossible—such as spelling, memorizing, or sustaining attention—become not only possible but easy.

Limited access to cerebral
functions determines
one's behavior.

Chapter Two

How to Tell If There's
Dysfunction in the Brain

My clinical experience indicates that an individual's behavior reflects the degree of access and integration of his cerebral functions. To a large degree, whether the functions are accessed—or not accessed—determines how a person behaves.

A person's behavior tells us the truth about how his brain functions. When someone says, "I hate reading [or mathematics or English, or fill in the blank]," he is actually telling us, "I cannot access the part of the brain I need to do that task easily." He hates it because it is difficult for him to do.

When we "hate" doing a task such as reading, spelling, or mathematics, it is usually because we find that task difficult to perform. When we can read well and easily, we usually don't avoid reading but rather seek it out because there is so much to learn and enjoy in books. But when children find reading demanding and stressful, they soon develop avoidance mechanisms. For instance, they might label reading as "boring." And who wants to do something that is boring?

What to Look For: Immaturity, Unusual Locomotion, or Lack of Coordination

A child who is Gestalt-dominant—that is, mostly using the creative, emotional side of her brain—and who has poor access to logical functions, such as cause-and-effect thinking, concrete reasoning, physical coordination, and so on, will often be perceived as "emotionally immature." (See the section "Major Patterns of Specific Learning Difficulties" Page 50 for a typical description of Gestalt dominance.) We make this assessment because emotional maturity is essentially the ability to modulate and control the expression of emotions based on a logical analysis of circumstances. A well-integrated person with good access to all cerebral functions may feel angry (largely a Gestalt experience) but will be able to make the rational judgment that now is not the appropriate time to express that anger (a logic experience). A Gestalt-dominant person with poor access to logic function, by contrast, will experience the anger and tend to act on that feeling with little consideration of the logical consequences.

When we are born only the Gestalt functions of the brain are activated. Then, around two years of age, we start to realize we can impact our world because the logic side of the brain begins to become active. Before this, we may learn to associate that if we cry, our caregiver will come, but making this association is not the same as following a logical series of events. A two-year-old only knows "now" and has no concept of "later," which is why it can be so frustrating to try to reason with a toddler. (As most parents learn, we shouldn't try and reason with toddlers about consequences but just distract them!) As logic becomes more active, we learn cause-and-effect relationships and eventually develop the ability to rationalize. Children who don't develop their logic functions are often called emotionally immature and are left behind their peers socially. Their behavior often shows little or no understanding about the consequences of their actions. For instance, they might climb up a tree, higher and higher, not realizing they can't get down until it's too late. Then they may fall or cry for help, with no real understanding that their own actions have put them in this situation. They are just as likely to repeat this mistake sometime in the future, perhaps frequently.

The caregivers of children with limited logic functions are especially at a loss as the children grow larger. No longer can the youngsters simply be picked up and carried away from the situation when unacceptable behavior arises. It is important to recognize that the inappropriate behavior isn't deliberate or malicious. Rather, the behavior occurs because the children simply cannot inhibit their actions, for they lack the cognitive skills available only through logic functions in the brain.

Even before children can talk, their actions can speak loudly about the degree of efficiency or inefficiency in their brain processing. Consider babies who never crawl or who develop "butt-scooting" methods of locomotion by their first birthday. What we know about the two halves of the brain, right and left, is that they control the opposite sides of the body (the right brain controls the left foot, for example). Crawling activates right brain–left brain integration to enable walking to develop easily (although just because a child has crawled or walked properly doesn't necessarily mean he won't have a learning difficulty). But babies who struggle with early locomotion are often manifesting an outward display of an inner confusion deep within the brain.

> Even before children can talk, their actions can speak loudly about the degree of efficiency or inefficiency in their brain processing.

Max

Take the case of Max, who was almost thirteen when I met him in October 1999. As a baby, Max never crawled but walked "like a crab" on his hands and toes and then began walking upright at eleven months. The crawling stage is considered critical for activating the corpus callosum, which connects the two hemispheres of the brain, and it allows the coordination of brain functions as well as physical coordination. Through muscle testing, I found that Max had been emotionally stressed when he was two years old and had switched, at a functional level, the right side of his brain to the left side and vice versa. Thus, there was confusion about which side of his brain processed logic functions and which side processed creative, or Gestalt, functions; the messages being sent were crossed from right to left and left to right.

On Crossinology's behavioral checklist (see Appendix A), Max's mother indicated he had allergies, was clumsy, and had problems with balance. He lacked coordination needed for sports or rhythmic activities. He scrawled like a first-grader although he was in the eighth grade. His grades were quite good, but he struggled with reading and spent most of his time in class doodling.

Two years later, things had turned around dramatically for Max. Out of 250 students in his high school, he had won the sophomore English award, an achievement that was especially significant for someone who had previously struggled with reading. He had a 3.75 grade-point average and was earning advanced scores on the statewide standardized tests. He found both the work and the tests relatively easy. He was taking Advanced Placement history, with lots of reading, and doing well. Max was using his lifelong love of language to study new languages—such as Tibetan and Japanese—on his own, independent of school. Once a classroom doodler who wasn't realizing his potential, he was now headed for a richly rewarding scholarly experience.

Avoiding difficult, stressful tasks

When someone has poor access to or poor integration of specific brain functions, he usually experiences difficulty in performing tasks that are dependent upon these functions. Difficulty performing these tasks will almost always generate stress whenever they are attempted, often resulting in avoidance behaviors. The extent of the avoidance behaviors usually relates to the degree of stress generated when attempting to access and integrate the relevant functions. For example, children whose brain "wiring" is deficient for short-term visual memory will find memorizing spelling lists very stressful and unrewarding. Consequently, they will avoid doing it at all costs, spending their time on activities such as computer games instead. Or if they are slow in reading and completing tasks, they will find anything more interesting than their homework—even taking the dog for a walk. They procrastinate and constantly turn in their homework assignments late.

> Difficulty performing (these) tasks will almost always generate stress whenever they are attempted, often resulting in avoidance behaviors.

What is most frustrating to schoolchildren, their parents, and teachers, not to mention employees and supervisors later in life, is that these avoidance behaviors are misinterpreted as just that—avoiding the work. But in reality, they are signals that the brain is misfunctioning. Then the vicious cycle begins: the more punishment the children receive for not wanting to do their work, the more stress becomes associated with the task. Accomplishing the task is not a simple matter of trying harder. *Most of the time, these students are trying as hard as they can and are still not experiencing success.* Many people with learning difficulties don't have any idea that they are not performing at an optimal level. They just know that they'd much rather play on the computer, give the dog a bath, or water the plants than get down to business. They don't hand in their homework, do the readings, or study for spelling tests—and they can find an infinite number of excuses to avoid these tasks.

We need to learn to interpret this avoidance behavior for what it is—a cry for help. The child is saying, "This is difficult. I'm have trouble doing this work; that's why I'm behaving this way and avoiding it." As stated before, when the tasks are *easy* to perform, learning is fun and work gets done; children perform well on tests and are rewarded for that behavior.

> Avoidance behavior is a cry for help.

My experience shows that many of the people having the greatest difficulty with "learning" are often innately quite clever. They just cannot access the specific brain functions they need to perform certain tasks they are required to do. In talking with these people and listening to the questions they ask, it is obvious they are sharp, intelligent people.

If a clearly bright person does not read or spell well or has great difficulty understanding and doing even simple mathematics, a reasonable assumption is that she just isn't concentrating or paying attention or trying hard enough.

What is overlooked is that intelligent people may, in fact, be unable to access the relevant brain function when needed or may only be able to do so when not under duress. Parents of such children are often told by well-meaning advisers to enroll them in technical or trade schools where they can use their hands and won't need to read or write.

Perhaps an analogy will help to illustrate this point. If we ask children if they know how to run, most would answer "yes." If we went further and asked, "Will you run for me?" they would likely reply, "Sure, where do you want us to run to?" However, if their legs were tied, they might still answer "yes" (of course they know *how*), but they would be *unable* to do so. If you just ignored their tied-up legs (or, stated another way, their lack of access to making their legs function) and said, "Come on now, run down the block," they would likely become frustrated and angry because they *could* run down the block if only they were able to use their tied-up legs!

The difference between this analogy and the lack of access to brain functions is that a child would clearly understand her inability to run and would be able to say, "If you would just untie my legs, I'll gladly run down the block for you." She would be able to let you know why she can't do what is asked of her. This communication would help alleviate the frustration (stress) of not being able to perform the task.

However, when there is a lack of access to specific brain functions, neither the affected individual nor those around her can understand why she cannot perform certain tasks dependent upon the specific brain functions not being accessed. The difficulty is completely invisible and often undiagnosed. Telling her to try harder is a meaningless command.

Children almost never consciously know why they can't access specific brain functions and consequently get frustrated. This situation often leads to anger, and that anger often leads to inappropriate behavior.

> Children almost never consciously know why they can't access specific brain functions and consequently get frustrated. This situation often leads to anger, and that anger often leads to inappropriate behavior.

Taylor

One boy I treated, a ten-year-old named Taylor, frequently lashed out at his classmates when they hurt his feelings, often inadvertently, at school. Taylor had been diagnosed with ADD and was taking Ritalin. He came for BIT treatment in mid-March 2003 and subsequently they decided he should stop taking the drug. Soon after, his mother e-mailed me about his remarkable progress. On March 23, she wrote:

Things are progressing so quickly we can't believe it. Today Taylor did two pages of his Kumon [a Japanese math drill] and only had two questions wrong—usually he would have around 50 to 60 percent errors. And the time spent doing those two pages has gone from three hours to one hour. I think as he gains confidence he'll pick up the speed. Life in our household has been so happy. His attitude is very positive and tasks get done quickly and correctly. He loves to do things that make me cry with happiness. ...

Tomorrow is a big test as it will be the first day back at school. And Tay is going to go Ritalin-free!! He is really easy to live with now and doesn't get into everything like he used to. Our life has changed so much in such a short time. Thank you, thank you, thank you!

She wrote again on March 28:

Taylor's teacher talked to me yesterday about how Tay is doing in school. Although he still has difficulty transitioning from one task to another (and if he is really honed in on something it is difficult to get him to let go of the idea or item), he is much more relaxed and laid back. He hasn't had any altercations with other students—and that used to be a daily [consequence] of getting his feelings hurt. ...

Some surprises: Taylor actually volunteered to do an extra day of Kumon math homework because he had forgotten some of his other homework at school and this was one way for him to make amends. Yesterday I came home from my workout at 6:30 a.m. and there was Tay doing his Kumon—totally of his own volition. Did I mention that he had already eaten, dressed, brushed his teeth, and put on his socks by himself?

Her e-mail on March 31 included this information:

He is definitely happier and continues to do things that amaze me. His manners have improved so much, which makes it nicer to be with him, too. He actually had fun doing some of his homework this weekend. As an experiment, he tried one Ritalin on Saturday to see how it would affect him. He was able to stay concentrated for a longer period of time and work more independently. However, when the meds were wearing off he was such a bear. I don't think I want to do that again. So we are back to a meds-free approach. Am I correct in thinking he'll continue to improve and his attention and focus will get better with more time under his belt?

The answer to her last question was yes, his attention span and focus would improve as he gained maturity. Commonly, a sudden physical and emotional maturation process happens immediately after treatment. When the brain function is allowed to mature to its age-appropriate level, the body does a rapid "catch-up." After BIT treatment, these children make leaps in physical maturity and independence, and they begin to see themselves as confident, competent individuals who are better able to cope with their emotions.

Living a Medicine-Free, Attention-Deficit-Free Life

Alex

Carol M.'s ten-year-old son, Alex, had been diagnosed with ADHD and put on Ritalin at age nine. She brought him to me from their home in California for a weekend of intensive therapy. After ten hours of treatment, she stopped giving him Ritalin "cold turkey." No one ever suspected her son wasn't using the medication anymore because his behavior was normal, and he went from making Cs and Ds in school to earning Bs. The treatment changed her son's life. As Carol says, "The liberation from a lifelong label is a priceless gift. It allows the child to create a life that is driven by their passion and not their arbitrary diagnosis."

Kyle

In another case, a mother—at her wit's end—brought her seventeen-year-old son, Kyle, from Indiana for a weekend of intensive treatment. He suffered from very poor access to the logic functions in his brain, which was corrected during the treatment. Afterward, his mom told me that, for the first time, he took the initiative to pack his bag when it was time to go home. Packing a bag is something that most of us take for granted, but for this boy, the task had been out of the question. His failure to do the task wasn't simply recalcitrant teenage behavior; it was because, before treatment, he could never make the logical connection that we're going to make a trip, and therefore, I'd better gather the things I'll need to take. This simple example illustrates the sort of logic that had eluded him until his brain's logic center was unblocked through Brain

Integration Treatment. Clearly, his life has been dramatically improved.

Self-Motivation

Brett

Self-motivation to learn is an important factor. Just because you can now perform a learning task well does not mean that you *will*. Previous conditioning and the memory of "how it was" often shut off the will to try. Defusion techniques help restore the brain's natural desire to learn by removing the negative emotional experiences from the past. For instance, if test taking has always been traumatic, then the negative—and subconscious—emotional response to tests needs to be removed. Once the negative association has been eliminated, the brain will be able to function as it was meant to, without the psychological stumbling blocks that prevent people from reaching their full potential. A fifteen-year-old we treated showed no improvement in school after brain integration. We tested him, and he demonstrated his new ability to learn to spell any word quite easily and to remember it. He just didn't want to apply himself because of negative associations from earlier experiences. His improved brain functioning was showing up in other areas, however. He was now making seven out of ten baskets in basketball, whereas before treatment, he had been making only two or three.

> Defusion techniques help restore the brain's natural desire to learn by removing the negative emotional experiences from the past.

Major Patterns of Specific Learning Difficulties

Depending upon how limited a person's access is to certain Gestalt and logic functions, he or she will demonstrate one of the patterns, or mosaics, discussed in the following sections. Each pattern indicates a lack of access or a specific learning difficulty. These are general models, since no two people with dyslexia or ADD will function exactly the same and their individual strengths and weaknesses will vary.

Gestalt Dominance (or ADD)

The most frequently observed specific learning difficulty is Gestalt dominance or, as it is known more commonly, Attention Deficit Disorder.

ADD is indicated when a person cannot perform a series of sequential tasks, any one of which he can do easily. A person suffering from ADD is not able to complete the series of tasks, not because he cannot perform them but because he loses concentration or is easily distracted. He is unable to keep his attention on completing the entire series.

We might, for example, tell a child with ADD to go to her room, pick up her toys, remove the dirty laundry, and come back with her homework assignments. But when she gets to the door of her room, she is distracted by something in the room and forgets everything else. The child is not deliberately disobedient but is simply unable to remember a series of instructions—instructions that are processed by the logic hemisphere.

People with this pattern of learning dysfunction have good access to most Gestalt functions but poor access to logic. For these individuals, the Gestalt hemisphere dominates information processing, and the normal balance provided by complementary logic functions is largely absent.

People with ADD and Gestalt dominance consistently display the following behavioral symptoms as the rule, rather than the exception, in their daily behavior:

- *They are impulsive, acting without thinking.* If they see something they want on the other side of the road, they run across without looking for traffic.

- *They have little understanding of the connection between cause and effect.* If they want to do X, they do it, never thinking "What will happen if I do?" They may push a sibling at the top of the stairs, not realizing that the sibling could fall down and be injured.

- *They have difficulty in budgeting time.* They often leave projects incomplete because of they don't have a sense of time—let alone the ability to budget it. Combined with their lack of concentration, this deficit is often expressed as poor organizational skills.

- *They have difficulty concentrating.* Concentration is merely paying attention over time. If there is no "sense of time," they are unable to pay attention to it.

- *They have difficulty spelling.* Generally, they spell phonetically by putting letters together until they "sound" like the word.

This strategy works as long as the word is spelled just as it sounds; however, many words in the English language rely on our ability to visualize the word in our heads, from memory—an ability that exists only in the logic hemisphere. This function is not to be confused with creative visualization, a Gestalt process whereby we can imagine an image.

- *They have difficulty with arithmetic.* They have trouble remembering multiplication tables and understanding mathematical concepts. Much of math derives from logic; therefore, a weak logic hemisphere will result in problems with math. Higher-level mathematics uses both logic and Gestalt functions.

- *They have difficulty in comprehending what is read.* Although their reading may appear to be fluent, they do not immediately process the meaning of what they have read. They may have to read and reread a passage until they get it. They may be able to intepret symbols (a Gestalt function), but they have difficulty assigning meaning to the words/symbols interpreted (a logic function).

- *They have good physical coordination.* They may even be gifted athletically. Gestalt functions control body awareness, balance, running, and orientation in space; therefore, a dominance of these brain functions tends to be manifested in good physical skills. Furthermore, if this is one of the few areas in which success is experienced, they tend to devote a great deal of their time and practice to it. Think of the sports jock who hates schoolwork.

It is precisely because of these symptoms that people displaying Gestalt-dominant processing are found to have an attention deficit. They have difficulty in single-focus attention; instead, they attend to everything and everyone.

Often, children with ADD never learn to read well despite the best efforts of teachers, tutors, and other professionals. Tutoring either doesn't work or is painfully slow. With dysfunction in the brain circuitry, the tutoring only "reaches" the small percentage of the brain that functions. And when critical pathways are not open at all, the student cannot make sense of the tutor's explanation, no matter how patient both parties are. Put another way, a student with learning difficulties lacks the basic alphabet or processor to serve as an interpreter or dictionary for the language used in tutoring. For example, it's difficult, if not impossible, to understand the concept of algebra if the brain areas responsible for abstract concepts are inaccessible. Without that foundation, the tutor might as well be (and, to the frustrated student, often seems to be) speaking in a foreign language. Only through the restoration of brain functions—the renormalization of the pathways—can effective learning take place.

Surviving a childhood marked by learning difficulties often makes a person resilient in later life. He is able to intuit potential outcomes and is not restricted by the logical, step-by-step process employed by sequential thinkers. He is sometimes a risk-taker because he is not limited by a logical mind that foresees possible problems. He uses his people skills to succeed and employs others to do the reading and writing.

Logic Dominance

A much less common learning difficulty involves logic dominance.

 People who can access their logic functions but have difficulty accessing their Gestalt functions are the "true" dyslexics, according to the standard psychological definition.

People with logic dominance are usually good at arithmetic up to at least the level of algebra, as long as the problems require concrete, rather than abstract, reasoning. They can concentrate and follow sequential directions well. However, they may have to be taught things that other people learn unconsciously, such as intuitive reasoning and social skills.

These individuals tend to display the following four behaviors most, if not all, of the time:

They have an inability to spell well. They may spell phonetically by putting letters together to "sound" like the word is pronounced—not a successful strategy in the English language. Words such as o-n-e differ dramatically when compared to the sound of the individual letters w-u-n.

- *They have great difficulty in reading.* They usually stumble over words and misread words. Sounding out words is a slow and unsuccessful procedure for them, especially because many English words do not sound as they are spelled. However, these children tend to have excellent reading comprehension because they have to read so slowly.

- *They have dysrhythmia.*
  They are unable to clap
  or tap a tune.

- *They lack physical coordination.* They tend to be
  extremely clumsy and are
  always having accidents.

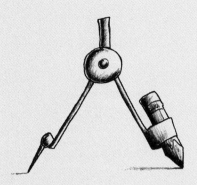

Limited Access to Both Gestalt and Logic Functions

People who have limited access to both their Gestalt and their
logic functions have severe learning difficulties and a great deal of
confusion in their cerebral processing. They are often low-
functioning, developmentally disabled individuals or appear to be
so, but when integrated, they become "normal" in their function.

With either Gestalt or logic dominance, the person can at least
compensate for the functions she cannot access. Thus, the Gestalt-
dominant person may be highly intuitive and possess good people
skills, and the logic-dominant person may be able to follow step-
by-step instructions and use a computer well. But when a person
has poor access to both hemispheres, the brain's ability to compensate for these deficits is extremely limited.

Children with poor access to both of the brain's hemispheres often
demonstrate the following characteristics:

- *They are extremely delayed in developing and using language.* For
  example, an eight-year-old child may only recognize three letters and two numbers.

- *They are significantly delayed in reading ability.* They often have difficulty even recognizing words.

- *They demonstrate significant problems with spelling.* Words with more than three or four letters become impossible to spell.

- They have difficulty understanding numbers or even basic arithmetic. Learning to count, adding and subtracting, and remembering the days of the week are all very difficult tasks.

- *They have little or no concentration or focus.* They appear "off in the clouds" or "spaced out."

- *They appear "confused" or are misinterpreted as "lazy" or just plain "slow."* Often, they seem to be fairly apathetic and lethargic, with no zest for life.

Limited Integration of Gestalt and Logic Functions

People who have good access to both their Gestalt and logic functions but limited integration of these functions display the least common pattern of learning difficulties, mainly because they display the least dysfunction.

But for children with poor integration of both hemispheres, school is frequently an extremely frustrating experience. They can often perform most tasks well, except when the tasks require good integration. Since coordination of Gestalt and logic functions is required for reading and spelling, they avoid these essential academic tasks because dealing with the lack of synthesis is too stressful.

The lack of coordination between Gestalt and logic functions often limits what functions they can access, producing learning dysfunctions similar to those seen in people who have poor access to either one of the hemispheres.

These individuals tend to display the following behaviors:

- *They have extreme difficulty with reading.* Reading is so stressful that they can only do it for a few minutes at a time or else avoid it completely. As adults, they read what they have to but almost never read for pleasure.

- *They spell phonetically.* They spell words like they sound, unable to visualize the proper spelling in the mind's eye.

- *They have difficulty with higher mathematics (algebra and beyond),* even though they may perform basic arithmetic perfectly.

As adults, these people are often more successful than others in the categories mentioned here because they can compensate more efficiently. They usually limit their activities to tasks that are either more logical or more Gestalt in nature.

People with dyslexia and ADD do not grow out of their difficulties but learn to compensate for them by avoiding tasks that they find difficult. Supportive parents and teachers are a tremendous asset to children with learning difficulties, especially if these children do not receive any formal intervention. Helpful caregivers will focus on the positive aspects—what their children can do as opposed to what they can't do.

Often, a person who is able to compensate for his deficits will perform at an acceptable level, albeit one that is nowhere near his potential. Such an individual is often ineligible for any remedial help or conventional invervention because he is "too functional."

Joseph

Joseph, a thirteen-year-old, fit into this "too functional" category when he came to me for treatment. Although he was a good student, he was fully aware that he wasn't performing at his optimal ability. (He was unusual in this regard. Most children are not aware that they could be functioning better; they just assume it's the way they are and that's that). Joseph was able to fine-tune his skills when he received treatment that restored the integration of his brain functions. After the treatment, he returned to school and was the only student in his class who was able to memorize a five-minute oral presentation. His teacher was amazed; she knew that Joseph was bright but never expected he'd be able to memorize a lengthy speech. Brain Integration Technique had enabled him to fully access his logic functions and integrate both hemispheres of his brain, abilities that are critical for memorization.

Muscle testing, also known as
kinesiology—is the study of
muscles and their movement

Chapter Three

How Muscle Testing and Applied Physiology Developed

The Origins of Muscle Testing

The Introduction of Kinesiology by R. W. Lovett (1932)

Muscle testing, also known as kinesiology—the study of muscles and their movement—was introduced in the early twentieth century by R. W. Lovett, an orthopedic surgeon in Boston who was interested in analyzing difficulties resulting from polio and spinal nerve damage.[4] Using muscle testing, he was able to detect spinal nerve damage by observing that the muscles testing "weak" (or unable to resist when pressure was applied to them) often had the

---

4   A.T. Legg, "Physical Therapy in Infantile Paralysis." *In Principles of Practice of Physical Therapy*, vol 2, p. 45. (Hagerstown, MD: Mocked, W. F. Prior Company, 1932).

same spinal nerve innervating them. (See the section "More on Muscle Testing" for a fuller description of this process.)

Academic Kinesiology and the Work of Henry and Florence Kendall, George Goodheart, and Frank Chapman (1930s and 1940s)

In the 1940s, Henry and Florence Kendall further developed Lovett's work, and the field of academic kinesiology was born—a new science that analyzed muscle movement and the way in which muscles move joints. George Goodheart, a chiropractor from Detroit, became interested in this new science. He observed that when joints and bones moved in abnormal ways, corresponding muscles were "weak." But by massaging both ends of a muscle where it attached to the bones, he was able to elicit a "strong" response from the muscle. He also noticed that various diseases would make specific muscles test weak. However, although his muscle-massage technique worked some of the time, it did not always change the muscle to elicit a strong response. He read the work of an American osteopath, Frank Chapman, who suggested that sluggish lymph flow was associated with various symptoms of disease. Chapman had discovered a system of points on the body (the Chapman Reflex Points, published in the 1930s) that were related to specific disease conditions and were tender when massaged. Regular massage therapy applied to these points not only made them less tender but also lessened the disease symptoms. Goodheart added the Chapman Reflex Points to his system and kept searching for more factors that might help his patients.

Terence Bennett's Work on Blood Flow (1930s)

Terence Bennett, another American chiropractor, had a different system of reflex points for promoting blood flow that he theorized had an impact on health. His model, also published in the 1930s, was based on the principle that oxygen and nutrients must get to individual cells for good health. Since it is the blood that carries oxygen and nutrients to the body tissues, he investigated whether efficient blood flow had an impact on health. Bennett was able to prove his theories using radiopaque dyes injected into volunteers' blood so that the blood flow was visible on X rays. Then he would have the subjects lie down under a fluoroscope to observe that holding their reflex points changed their blood flow.

Applied Kinesiology

And so the new science of applied kinesiology began. It combined the Chapman Reflex Points for lymphatic function, Bennett's points for vascular function, the origin/insertion (that is, where each end of the muscle attaches to bone) approach for muscular problems, and muscle testing for biofeedback in both diagnosis and therapy.

East and West Combine: Goodheart's Work in the 1960s

In the late 1960s, Goodheart began reading Chinese medical literature about the Acupuncture Meridian system, which the Chinese said mapped the flow of energy throughout the body. For thousands of years, the Chinese had been observing empirically the energetic system of the body. They had developed an understanding of the principles by which the energy flowed and how to manipulate it. In fact, between the first century B.C. and the first century A.D., the Chinese method of manipulating the energy imbalances in the body was documented in the Huang Di Nei Ching (Yellow Emperor's Inner Classic of Medicine). This book was based on a thousand years of accumulated knowledge. The Chinese had observed a relationship between the meridians, where the acupuncture points are and the internal organs, which Goodheart was now able to connect to his mucle-response technique. Through direct muscle feedback, he could quickly and consistently discover the energy balance of the meridians and their associated organs.

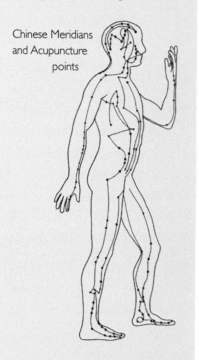

Chinese Meridians and Acupuncture points

Richard Utt and the International Institute of Applied Physiology

Since Goodheart developed his work, many other individuals have made important discoveries that have added to the developing field of kinesiology. Richard Utt is one of these individuals and the practitioner who taught me the most along the path that brought me to where I am today.

Utt is the founder and president of the International Institute of Applied Physiology in Tucson, Arizona. He was an aircraft electrical engineer before turning to this field. His engineering background led him to take a very scientific approach to kinesiology, whereby he developed Applied Physiology. As a student of his, I studied cadavers and learned about each muscle in the body. Consequently, I know very specific questions to "ask" through muscle testing in order to address very specific problems. Just as you might respond "I'm fine" to the broad question "How are you?" a more specific question such as "How is your little toe feeling after you stubbed it yesterday?" might reveal a very different response about your actual health. Effective treatment relies on precise muscle testing—that is, asking the right "questions."

Applied Physiology is a muscle-testing system that allows the practitioner to pinpoint specific stresses that impede function at the deepest levels of cellular activity. It allows access to tens of thousands of bits of information regarding the anatomy, physiology, attitudes, and emotions in individuals and, then, the ability to release any inhibiting energy. The system is based on the Chinese principles of energy but uses a Western format that allows for the manipulation of energy in any direction. A systematic investigation of the muscle system is conducted to evaluate the muscles' relationship to the meridian energy. Furthermore, stress is viewed in an entirely new way. Instead of something to automatically seek to eliminate, stress is now observed and understood so that individuals can consciously participate in its removal. A new perspective is also given on the "disease" state that traditionally has been considered the enemy.

Applied Physiology is a muscle-testing system that allows the practitioner to pinpoint specific stresses that impede function at the deepest levels of cellular activity

Applied Physiology considers disease the stressor that tells individuals when certain physical and metaphysical laws are being stretched. When disease or any other stressor is present, it must be rectified in order for the individual to continue to grow and move back to a healthy state. Mental, emotional, and physical well-being are the objectives. The template of the physical body is used to give clues about these areas, which are not visible but are tangible nonetheless.

How Can Muscle Testing Tell You Anything?

How can pushing on a muscle tell you anything you don't already know? The muscles are controlled by the subconscious (or, in the vocabulary of psychologists, the unconscious) mind. If you are walking to a friend's house, planning what you are doing for dinner tonight, you aren't consciously telling your limbs to move, one

after the other. All you have done is told the body to walk; the "program" for doing this task is something you learned as a toddler, and it is now stored in the brain as a series of instructions that are performed in a sequence automatically, as part of your subconscious. The subconscious receives 5 to 10 million sensory inputs per second just to keep the body functioning, and if we had to consciously think about the process, we wouldn't have time to do anything else. The subconscious enables us to do everyday actions while our thoughts are focused elsewhere. In other words, the muscles are linked to the subconscious.

> The subconscious enables us to do everyday actions while our thoughts are focused elsewhere. In other words, the muscles are linked to the subconscious.

Muscle testing uses this linkage to obtain information that is stored in the subconscious. Not only is the subconscious running the muscles, it is also controlling all internal and external body functions, maintaining a stable internal body temperature, regulating which parts of the brain are active and connected to the other appropriate parts of the brain for full function, storing the memories of everything that has ever happened to us, and so on.

Applying this connection enables a practitioner to use the muscles to retrieve information from the subconscious through various acupressure points in specific combinations on the body while simultaneously performing the muscle testing. The muscles give either a locked or unlocked response, indicating stress or no stress, yes or no, active or not active, depending on what is being "asked" of them by the practitioner. This biofeedback comes directly from the person being tested, without the need for any subjective interpretation from the practitioner.

Being able to access and remove subconscious stress is one of the most powerful aspects of muscle testing as it is practiced today.

Considering that stressors are often subconscious, a previously undetected stress could be the factor that is blocking neurological flow, thus preventing information from moving to the necessary areas of the brain for processing. And once the stress is removed, so is the blockage. Being able to access and remove subconscious stress is one of the most powerful aspects of muscle testing as it is practiced today.

BIT can eradicate learning difficulties ... and restore the innate
ability to learn, dramatically
affecting how well one functions
not only in the classroom but
also in all aspects of life.

Chapter Four

Understanding Crossinology's BIT

The Origins of Crossinology's Brain Integration Technique

The Brain Integration Technique was initially developed in 1988 at my learning center in Melbourne, Australia. In 1996, I earned advanced degrees in neuroscience and psychology. During that time, I wrote two major theses and conducted extensive scientific research and brain scanning that validated the efficacy of the BIT learning-correction program. Although the number of subjects in my research was small, the studies provided strong evidence that the treatment normalized brain-wave activity and generated statis-tically significant improvement on standard psychometric tests of intellectual performance. And even more important, clinical symp-toms disappeared following BIT treatment (see Appendix B for an overview of the studies).

The Brain Integration Technique that was begun in Australia has been further refined at the Learning Enhancement Center in the United States. BIT can eradicate learning difficulties such as ADD, ADHD, and dyslexia and restore the innate ability to learn, dramatically affecting how well one functions not only in the classroom but also in all aspects of life. It improves the abilities to read with greater comprehension, learn and retain spelling words, understand mathematical concepts, and become physically coordinated, all of which build newfound confidence. It is especially beneficial to executives who want to improve their organizational skills, problem-solving abilities, and interpersonal relationships. Athletes can expect benefits in terms of hand-eye coordination, gross and fine motor skills, stamina, and energy levels. Even children with autism, developmental delays, Fragile X Syndrome, and spina bifida have experienced improvement in their capabilities after BIT treatment. And people who have suffered closed-head injuries through accidents or strokes or who have lost function after the removal of brain tumors are likely to see improvement—often complete restoration of function—after BIT treatment, depending on the degree of brain damage that has been sustained.

The Nature of Specific Learning Difficulties

Typical symptoms of a learning difficulty, no matter whether it's labeled dyslexia or ADD (with or without hyperactivity), or something else, involve troubles with spelling, reading, and writing. But there are often other associated problems, such as difficulties with math skills, auditory processing, organizational skills, and interpersonal skills, as well as various types of memory deficits. Individuals vary in their difficulties and tend to have their own unique mosaics of deficits.

People often associate learning difficulties with a low IQ or even mental retardation, but in many cases, such prejudices are decidedly incorrect. Although a person with learning difficulties cannot learn in the conventional way, his problems are quite independent from his thinking ability or IQ. Individuals with learning difficulties are often gifted at intuitively knowing the correct answer or the right business decision, and they make great entrepreneurs, frequently leading the population toward innovative ideas and products.

> Although a person with learning difficulties cannot learn in the conventional way, his problems are quite independent from his thinking ability or IQ.

If there is equal and integrated access to all brain functions in both cerebral hemispheres, then people perform well in all areas of learning. However, if, for any reason, they cannot access specific brain functions, they will have difficulty performing tasks that involve or depend upon those functions. They commonly choose occupations that let them capitalize on their verbal skills in communication (such as sales or marketing), or they choose to do something creative with their hands, allowing them to move around. Desk jobs are too restrictive for them.

If they don't find a positive, productive niche for themselves, they may be unable to maintain good self-esteem. Students with learning difficulties may become so discouraged by their lack of success in school that their self-esteem plummets along with their test scores; they stop trying, and they may turn to illegal means of coping with the demands of life, such as drugs or crime. In fact, the prisons are full of people with learning difficulties who can't read or write. A startling 70 percent of recidivised individuals in the United States—people who have served jail terms and then become reincarcerated—are illiterate.[5] Furthermore, a 1990 study by the U.S. Department of Education showed that children with early antisocial behavior and ADHD are at greater risk for teenage drug use and dependence.[6] Youngsters with learning difficulties are either defeated by their early negative experiences in school or become more determined to succeed, depending in part upon their personalities.

Standard Psychological Tests Show Which Brain Functions Are Having Difficulty

Some clients who seek BIT treatment have already been through a battery of testing that gives the BIT practitioner information about which areas of the brain are functioning—or not functioning. In addition to getting immediate feedback through muscle testing, the

---

5   As cited in the video "Among the People: Facing Poverty in America," (Washington, DC: U.S. Conference of Catholic Bishops, 2002).

6   See B. P. Casemore's *Teen Drug Use: Impacts and Outcomes* (Washington, DC: U.S. Department of Education Office of Educational Research and Improvement, 1990).

BIT practitioner can explain to the client how his brain is functioning and why he is having difficulties in certain areas.

Standard psychological tests evaluate specific learning problems and determine what types of cerebral functions and processes *can be* accessed and to what extent these functions actually *are* accessed. These tests include the Wechsler Intelligence Scale for Children-Revised (WISC IIIR), the Wechsler Adult Intelligence Scale (WAIS), and the Stanford Binet Intelligence Scale. They contain an array of carefully devised tasks that are generally divided into two groups: verbal subtests and performance subtests.

The verbal subtests involve tasks that require access to functions that are predominantly logic-based, although some of these subtests require access to only a few logic functions. Others require access to logic and Gestalt functions simultaneously but with the "lead" functions contributed by the logic hemisphere of the brain. Likewise, some of the performance subtests involve tasks that require access to only Gestalt functions, whereas others require integrated functions with a Gestalt lead.

The score on each subtest reveals the degree to which a person can access the specific functions required to perform that subtest. Poor scores indicate which types of functions the individual has difficulty accessing. Trouble with accessing specific functions has been correlated with poor performance in certain academic areas: for example, someone with limited access to logic functions will typically perform at a substandard level in spelling and/or math. Spiky WISC scores—

that is, scores that are dramatically lower on certain subtests than others—are often an indication of a learning difficulty.

Crossinology's Brain Integration Technique Restores Brain Functions

Once we understand which brain functions control which information-processing tasks, all we need to do is unblock the pathways that are causing learning difficulties. In a sense, it is like fine-tuning the computer hardware so that the software package can run as it's supposed to. The only limitation, of course, is if there are physiological problems with the hardware—or, in our context, brain damage; if damage exists, then the software won't run because some of the physical connectors are broken.

How Brain Integration Works

Practitioners with specialized training in muscle testing and acupressure can locate, with the BIT assessment, blocks in information flow within the brain. As I noted earlier, such blockages are frequently due to certain types of emotional stress, especially early in life, that affect various pathways in the brain. Human behavior scientists have identified this type of stress as the "fight-or-flight" reaction, which was developed as a survival mechanism by early humans. Under stress, the brain's blood supply is redirected into the body to allow a quick physical response to the threat, and the corpus callosum, which connects the right and left hemispheres, simply shuts down. This response is helpful if we are confronted with a truck that is about to hit us and we instinctively jump out of its way. However, when we are under emotional stress, we can become dysfunctional because we can't "think" clearly. When the corpus callosum isn't working properly due to the redirection of the brain's blood supply to be ready for flight, people often react like the proverbial deer in the headlights; they may temporarily freeze up, for example, while speaking in public or suffering from exam anxiety.

Traumas in Early Life

The Brain Integration Technique opens up the blockages that prevent the proper flow of blood in the brain and resets the brain's normal information-processing and problem-solving machinery. It utilizes the electromagnetic flow of information in the brain, ensuring that the information that comes in through the eyes and ears goes to the

> Some traumas early in life can leave the brain in a permanent state of "fight or flight."

correct location in the brain with the right sequence and timing. When this connection is established, brain function is restored to normal. Information is transferred to short-term memory and then on to long-term memory without any stress or effort at all.

More on Muscle Testing

Muscle testing is both a science—with rules, principles, and logical techniques—and an art—with skills that need to be developed to interpret the muscle response. Here is a basic description of how the testing is done. Two people are required: a subject and a practitioner. Normally, the subject stands erect and holds one arm up and out to the side, parallel to the floor, with the elbow straight. The practitioner faces the subject, rests one hand on the shoulder of the subject's resting arm for stability, and then places the other hand on the subject's extended arm, just above the wrist. The subject is told to resist while the practitioner applies downward pressure, gently but firmly, toward the floor. This exercise is not a strength test but a test to check the ability of the muscle to "lock," or resist the even pressure. A "strong" muscle locks or has firm resistance to the practitioner's pressure, and a "weak" muscle unlocks, meaning the practitioner is easily able to push the arm down.

Even though our conscious mind gives the overall instruction for what our body should do (such as walk, stand, etc.), in reality our muscles are controlled by the subconscious brain and are designed to lock or unlock in order for us to move, as well as to prevent physical damage. The subconscious element of muscle control can be readily understood in the everyday example of walking down the street, deep in conversation with a friend. Who is "running" your body? The subconscious handles the need to put down your right foot, then the left foot, and so forth, without you being aware of it. Or think of an Olympic weight lifter who has reached the breaking point, hoisting as much weight as his muscles can bear.

He desperately wants to win the gold medal, so there is no way that he is going to put down that weight. But the subconscious detects that if he continues, he is going to tear a tendon, muscle, or ligament, and thus, it overrides the conscious mind to protect the body from damage. Suddenly, he drops the barbells uncontrollably because all the muscles of the whole shoulder girdle have been unlocked by the subconscious part of the brain and he no longer has control over the muscles or the weight. Responses of this type are one way our bodies keep us from hurting ourselves. And this connection between the muscles and the subconscious allows muscle testing to provide biofeedback from the subconscious, measured before and after treatment, to determine if BIT treatment has been effective.

Even though our conscious mind gives the overall instruction for what our body should do (such as walk, stand, etc.), in reality our muscles are controlled by the subconscious brain and are designed to lock or unlock in order for us to move, as well as to prevent physical damage.

Each session usually lasts for one or two hours. To begin, the individual lies down, fully dressed, on a comfortable padded table, as standing for that long would be tiring for both the subject and the practitioner. Because it is the subconscious that is being treated, the individual's involvement throughout the procedure is fairly passive. In fact, some people even fall asleep. All of the roughly eighty steps that comprise the treatment are completely noninvasive.

Muscle testing is the first order of business in every step of the process. As described earlier, if the arm resists the pressure applied by the practitioner, it is judged strong. If it cannot resist the same amount of pressure, it is judged weak, which is an indication of stress or lack of function when identifying various brain areas. Just how closely our emotions are intertwined in our cognitive processes is illustrated by the fact that if the individual is asked to think of a positive experience—a pleasant or enjoyable thought—the muscle will test strong, and conversely, if the individual is asked to think of a negative experience—something unpleasant or dreaded—the muscle will test weak. The emotions appear to dominate our subconscious much more than was ever previously thought.

Different acupressure points related to different brain connections or disconnections are addressed at each stage. Muscle testing and retesting are done between each stage of the acupressure treatment to determine whether the procedure was effective, and the next step of the treatment can't begin until the last one is complete. Each treatment step is considered complete when a muscle that had previously responded weak now responds strong, thus indicating the stress has been removed and the area of brain function has been restored.

The practitioner collects signals from the individual and holds them (in much the same way that a computer's "clipboard" hangs on to information that has been copied from one section and then pastes it to another) while redistributing blood flow in the brain and reorganizing brain-wave patterns. Therefore, each acupressure holding is only related to the part of the brain being held on the clipboard at any one time. Pulse biofeedback, detected by the practitioner, indicates that this specific brain activity has been renormalized and that information is now flowing to the correct locations with the *appropriate patterning* or *timing*. This process is repeated for every part of the brain involved with learning.

A Typical Course of Treatment

The basic correction program takes approximately eight to twelve hours, an estimate based on the median time for treatment; the length of each person's program varies because of individual needs. Some people with only one or two areas of deficit may take just six hours to complete the whole program, whereas others with many areas of deficit need more time.

The first session of treatment includes an initial assessment that serves as a benchmark against which to evaluate future change. This assessment involves muscle testing to reveal the specific brain areas that need the most attention. At the end of the assessment (usually lasting about half an hour), we can tell the client the probable length of treatment required in her individual case.

Treatment then deals with the brain's deep-level switching—the pathways that handle right/left, front/back, and top/bottom processing. In deep-level switching problems, the brain becomes confused about the right and left hemispheres, which in turn creates confusion in logic and Gestalt processing. Front/back switching results in difficulty with resolving issues from the past, and top/bottom switching causes difficulty with getting out of a purely emotional response in order to develop a rational response. After switching pathways are addressed, treatment focuses on the degree of activation in the corpus callosum, so that the brain's two hemispheres can be used simultaneously.

The limbic system is treated early in the procedure, since it is the emotional filter through which the brain processes all information. As neurologist Antonio Damasio has shown, the limbic system assigns pleasure or pain to experiences and controls drive, motivation, and memory. Thus, it's important to address the limbic system in order to remove any emotional obstacles to these functions. Much like building a house, there is little sense in putting time and effort into creating a functional structure unless it rests on a solid foundation.

Treatment also deals with the eye muscles. Movement of the eye muscles activates memory. You can see this if you ask someone, "What did you do a week ago Tuesday?" Subconsciously, she will begin to move her eyes around while thinking of the answer. There should be no discomfort, aching, or pain in any eye position. Moving the eyes from side to side, or tracking, is critical for reading. If this action is stressful, tiredness will set in soon after you begin to read, and the next thing you know, you are asleep. The brain will always avoid stress if it can.

> The Brain Integration Technique clears the paths and resets the timing in brain functions.

The next part of the treatment focuses on the auditory processing, which uses both sides of the brain. The treatment coordinates information processed by the ears so that the subject can interpret what is heard and transfer it first into short-term and then into long-term memory. Next, we treat the sense of balance and the vestibular system, dealing with the semicircular canals imbedded in the skull next to the inner ear.

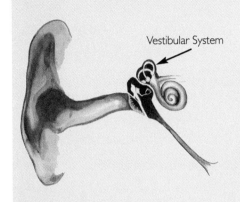

Vestibular System

Finally, treatment turns to marching, which involves the subject's ability to coordinate his body in both a contralateral and a homolateral way. When the subject steps forward with the left leg and swings the right arm forward at the same time, then the right leg and the left arm, he demonstrates contralateral movement; when the right arm and right leg move forward at the same time, then the left arm and left leg, he demonstrates homolateral movement. These movements are done while the practitioner addresses additional Gestalt and logic functions, so that the individual is able to process multiple functions simultaneously. This procedure will integrate and synchronize all the signals in the brain translating into the ability to multitask in the classroom or any other situation in life.

When these brain integration procedures are complete, we then apply specific learning corrections, if needed, for deficits in reading skills and comprehension, spelling, mathematics, and the whole range of cognitive tasks, such as matching patterns, foreground/background perception, and sequencing abilities.

All steps in the treatment deal with the subconscious level of the brain—things we can't control any more than we control our need to breathe. These subconscious barriers block effective learning. As I mentioned earlier, someone with a learning difficulty will unnecessarily (and subconsciously) transfer information back and forth between the hemispheres of the brain, resulting in very inefficient processing and the loss of information. Often, a person with a learning difficulty can only process a fraction of the information coming into his brain before treatment but 100 percent of it afterward.

The Gift of Normalized Brain Function: Real-Life Stories

What we are accomplishing through brain integration goes beyond merely improving test scores and enhancing the ability to perform in school. Rather, BIT involves a fundamental shift in one's self-image. It breaks down previous obstacles to full participation in society. If you aren't constantly preoccupied with trying to hide a learning difficulty, you're able to take notice of those around you. You're able to proceed with confidence in life, rather than with excuses. With good comprehension, the amount of time spent on reading is greatly reduced, freeing up time for other activities, such as new hobbies. Many clients I have treated report that they suddenly understand the joy of reading and are devouring every book they can get their hands on!

Stephen

Stephen, a sixteen-year-old boy I treated, was extremely frustrated with school; he passionately loved reading and was desperate to spell well when he sought treatment. He came to me for integration, and two weeks later, he had mastered 150 words that had always given him problems. At his next

> Many clients I have treated report that they suddenly understand the joy of reading and are devouring every book they can get their hands on!

appointment, he brought in a list of the 50 most difficult words and asked to be tested on them. He got all but 1 right. Six months later, he had no spelling problems of note and continued to be highly motivated in an area in which he had previously experienced only failure. Imagine the difference it makes to see oneself in a new light, no longer as a failure who always gets it wrong, even with a huge amount of unrewarded effort. Brain integration typically leads to an entirely new identity.

Amber

Amber received BIT treatment at age fifteen. She had never crawled as a baby, and she couldn't march, tie her shoes, or do jumping jacks even at age fifteen. By the eighth grade, she was still reading at the second-grade level. Before treatment, Amber says she was "in a cloud": "I was really lost. I had to be told over and over again what to do, and I would forget. [Now] I'm able to do everything. I can drive. I can read better. I can do my math, go on errands and remember stuff."

Doug

I once treated two siblings with learning difficulties. Their father sat in on their treatment sessions, as many parents do. While I was treating the children, the father revealed that he had always struggled with reading; anything beyond a magazine article was too tiring for him, and reading for pleasure was not a concept he knew. So, he decided to have BIT treatment himself. On their three-hour plane ride home, he read a whole paperback *for the first time in his life*. He discovered that reading was not boring; on the contrary, it was quite interesting, once his brain was able to function normally.

Self-Confidence Soars

Finally, consider the impact that test scores have in defining one's self-concept. Low test scores can be devastating. They can be used to place children permanently into a slower-paced curriculum, or track, that puts them further and further behind their peers. In Chapter One, I said that the WISC standardized test was widely used because of its high rate of test-retest reliability. However, some of the recipients of BIT treatment have disproven this assessment of the WISC's reliability, given the difference between their test results before brain integration and their retesting results afterward.

Jade

For instance, Jade, a ten-year-old I treated, had been born with brain damage and had such overwhelming learning difficulties that she scored in the first percentile (meaning she had a severe deficiency) among children her age for auditory short-term memory function. With virtually no short-term memory, she was having extreme difficulty learning anything at school. After integration (in this case, involving a lot of formatting of the hippocampus, an area deep in the brain involved with auditory and visual short-term memory), she soared to the fiftieth percentile for auditory short-term memory (meaning she was in the average range). Conventional wisdom about the WISC test suggested this sort of jump in scores was not possible. But since the girl could now access short-term memory, she could adequately learn her spelling words. For the first time in her life, she could recall her multiplica-

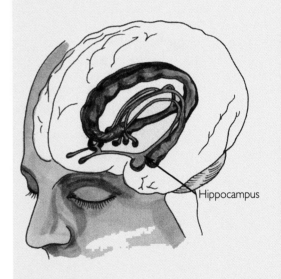

Hippocampus

tion tables consistently after learning them. She literally went from the bottom of her class to the top in six months. Imagine the impact on her self-confidence!

Organic Brain Damage

People who are developmentally delayed or have severe learning problems and major deficits in most areas of function—as indicated by low, average, borderline, or serious deficit rankings on standardized tests—may require more hours of treatment than those without severe deficits. My experience shows that even they will improve significantly in function, but their rate of improvement is slower than that for people with less severe deficits, and it is limited by the degree of brain damage they have.

Some brain damage is organic, meaning there is injured tissue in the brain; such injuries can occur before birth, during birth, or from a physical trauma after birth and cannot be treated. The degree of organic brain damage an individual has sustained can limit the amount of improvement that can be expected. However, many people suffer needlessly from additional confusion. This is where BIT treatment can improve one's ability to function in the world.

Jenna

Take, for example, the case of Jenna. While still in her mother's womb, Jenna's spine had failed to close properly, leaving her with mild spina bifida. She suffered from bladder and bowel incontinence as well as muscle paralysis and weakness in certain areas. Unable to use her legs well, she needed to use a wheelchair. However, she developed great upper-body strength and enjoyed doing karate.

When I met Jenna, she was twelve years old. Her learning difficulties stemmed mainly from poor reading comprehension, a lack of concentration, and an inability to budget time. She also was afraid of speaking in front of a group, lacked confidence, and had mood swings. Through biofeedback from muscle testing, I determined that Jenna had full access to her Gestalt functions but very little access to her logic functions: just 4 percent of her overall logic functions and 5 percent of the areas responsible for assigning meaning to words (reading comprehension) were accessible. She had 37 percent access to visual construction (needed for visualizing spelling words and times tables) and 53 percent access to concrete reasoning (needed for arithmetic functions). In addition, Jenna would benefit from correction to her corpus callosum, which had just 5 percent access to pathways before treatment.

Prior to treatment, her reading comprehension was zero—she remembered nothing of what she had just read (as would be expected from the minimal access to assigning meaning to words, as mentioned). After BIT treatment, Jenna's initial reading comprehension rose to 80 percent. And after a further application of BIT, her reading comprehension score was 95 percent. I was also able to correct the bladder incontinence problem that four previous surgeries had been unable to fix by strengthening her pelvic floor muscles with acupressure.

Three months later, after she'd resumed school in the fall, her first report card arrived. Jenna, who had previously received Cs, Bs, and a few As, had now earned two Bs, seven As, and an A plus in geography—a subject that requires good visual construction so the names of places can be memorized.

Maxine

Maxine was in her forties when I treated her for memory loss after a car accident. She had suffered disorientation and the loss of her extraordinary photographic memory following the accident. Recalling simple facts, such as the current president or the day of the week, became impossible. Making a shopping list or adding numbers was not manageable. And slowing down her car was no longer an automatic reflex. Instead, she had to remember how to lift her foot, press it on the pedal, and lift it off. Occupational and physical therapies hadn't helped.

After the first session of BIT treatment, Maxine noticed a difference. She completed ten sessions and regained her ability to learn and to function. She went on to complete a degree in computer information systems.

Johnny

In another case, a twenty-five-year-old man who had had a brain tumor removed came to me for treatment because he still couldn't walk or speak properly and was experiencing double vision. After he was treated with the Brain Integration Technique, there were dramatic improvements in each of these areas. Four years later, he strode into the room looking the picture of health. He was extremely happy and quite self-confident. And he was now doing a more complicated job: it turned out he'd always had a learning difficulty, and in the course of correcting the brain function problem, I had corrected the learning difficulty as well.

In some cases, the changes are not only inward and cognitive but outward and physical too, as the following case histories illustrate.

Gary

I once treated an adolescent boy from a family of farmers. His parents had assumed that, due to his limited mental capacity, poor eyesight, and stooped appearance, their son would always work on the farm. After treatment, his thinking abilities were so improved that his family realized he could attend a trade school, opening up a world of new possibilities because of the changes he experienced. Furthermore, he was able to stand up straight and walk without a stoop. Additionally, his eyesight was corrected, and he no longer needed glasses. It turned out that his eyesight problems were related to the external muscles of the eye. Poor vision due to weak external eye muscles is generally corrected, albeit inadvertently, by one of the steps in BIT treatment that specifically addresses those muscles.

> Poor vision due to weak external eye muscles is generally corrected, albeit inadvertently, by one of the steps in BIT treatment that specifically addresses those muscles.

Ian

In another case, a mother told me with amazement that she almost didn't recognize her son, whom I had recently treated, as she picked him up from school. His manner of walking had changed so much after brain normalization that, because she was sitting in a car and could not see his face, she didn't realize it was her own son until he stuck his head in the car window.

Having a well-integrated brain is essential to success in school, to psychological well-being, and to the ability to live life to its fullest potential—without the burden of a label that can carry a heavy penalty in our high-pressure, success-oriented world.

It can be horrible to constantly feel like a failure or to feel less smart than others, and it can be a real epiphany to realize all the struggling just comes from the brain's confused inner workings, over which one has no direct control. The gift of normalized brain function is what I hope to continue to pass on to others, so they, too, may live fuller lives as contributing members of society.

The costs of learning difficulties impact not only household finances and family life but also society as a whole.

Chapter Five

What the Future Holds

It brings tears of joy to my eyes when I see the results the Brain Integration Technique treatment has on others. There is unimaginable satisfaction in knowing that a person's life has dramatically changed in positive ways. Things she previously considered "impossible" are suddenly routine. Instead of dreading certain tasks or requirements in her life, she now proceeds full steam ahead. The metamorphosis is liberating: her self-image changes, her self-confidence soars, and she is able to make a contribution to her family and community, since her time and energy need not be devoted solely to coping with and compensating for her own difficulties. She no longer views herself as a "loser" or "retarded" or by any other negative label but rather as a normal, capable individual.

The costs of learning difficulties impact not only household finances and family life but also society as a whole. Spending on behavior medicines for children in the United States has now surpassed total spending on antibiotics and asthma medications for kids[7]. In 2003, 5.3 percent of our children were on medication for behavior problems such as ADD or depression. Besides the soaring costs of these drugs, side effects, such as loss of appetite and reduced growth, must also be considered. Thus, many parents have been searching for drug-free alternatives to treat learning and behavior difficulties.

Learning difficulties often result in unhappy, unsuccessful students and adults who are then tempted to self-medicate through drug and alcohol abuse or to vent their frustrations through violence. In fact, studies suggest that one-third to one-half of all people with ADD abuse alcohol. Learning difficulties also impose a burden on school systems trying to provide more paraprofessionals, special-education classes, or reading tutors. Programs for children who are unable to learn in a traditional class setting due to their learning difficulties consume a disproportionate amount of our schools' limited resources.

BIT treatment eliminates the need for costly prescriptions and the disruptions in children's lives that arise from the need to visit the school nurse for daily doses of behavior medicines. For some, it eliminates the need for placement in special-education programs and the stigma associated with that. It reduces the temptation to dull the pain of not succeeding in school or in life with drugs or alcohol. It helps restore harmony to one's psychological well-being and

---

7 Linda A. Johnson, "Spending Soars for Kids' Behavior Drugs," *Washington Post*, May 17, 2004.

improves interpersonal relationships with family and at school or work by removing the constant frustrations and tensions that can surround learning and behavior difficulties.

I envision a future in which every kindergartner in every school is evaluated by a trained BIT practitioner and treated if necessary. Early detection and correction would prepare the child with learning difficulties for a lifetime of successful learning, instead of frustration. Treatment would resolve a host of behavior problems that affect not only the child but also his or her classmates. When teachers spend a disproportionate amount of time and attention on students with learning difficulties and attention deficits, they have less time for the other children. The early resolution of learning difficulties would also prevent numerous problems in later years, I believe, potentially reducing the numbers of homeless, jailed, or chronically unemployed people.

> BIT treatment increases the number of people contributing their resources to society, rather than taking from it.

But to make this sort of a future a reality will require effort and commitment from people who feel compelled to get involved once they see or read about the dramatic improvements possible through the BIT approach. Obviously, training a large number of practitioners will be needed. Regional training centers for this purpose would have to be established and led by certified practitioners who can teach others. This methodology is still so young, however, that there are not yet enough certified practitioners.

At present, anyone interested in becoming a BIT practitioner would do well to complete a full series of courses in the Body Alignment Technique developed by Jeff Levin in Canada (www.bodyalignment.org). Levin should be contacted for international training and David Pasikov, M.A., in Boulder, CO (www.bodyalignment.net) for North American training. After being certified in this type of program, which takes about six to twelve months of weekend training (depending on how frequently the classes are run), the individual is ready for the training I offer in Brain Integration Technique, which is an intensive, two-week course. This additional training involves extensive physiological and neurological study based on both Western and Eastern approaches. In all, the training requires approximately one year of academic study interspersed with practical, hands-on experience.

> The ability to correct learning difficulties does exist, and it has worked for literally thousands of people.

I am forming a nonprofit organization that will handle future development for the Brain Integration Technique.

In the meantime, those who are seeking immediate help may wish to contact me through my website, www.crossinology.com. In addition, a list of recommended reading appears at the back of this volume.

In this book, I have attempted to give children and parents as well as other adults affected by learning difficulties answers and hope that should shine as a beacon of light in an otherwise foggy future, at least in academic terms. The ability to correct learning difficulties does exist, and it has worked for literally thousands of people. Those who seek permanent, noninvasive, nonmedicated solutions to correct—not merely compensate for—dyslexia, ADD, ADHD, and more are invited to join me in this revolutionary approach to optimizing brain function.

Appendix A

Behavioral Checklist for Learning Difficulties

At my clinic, Crossinology's Learning Enhancement Center, all clients (or their parents or guardians) are asked to complete a behavioral checklist. This list helps the practitioner identify the specific nature of the learning difficulty or other brain integration problems. The behaviors checked should be present most, if not all, of the time.

Items marked with an asterisk (*) tend to indicate that the dominant hemisphere for processing information is the Gestalt hemisphere (prevalent in so-called right-brain people); the other items tend to indicate the dominance of the logic hemisphere (seen in so-called left-brain people).

Directions: Please check anything which **might** apply, and put **two checks** next to anything which is especially important.

____ Accident prone

____ Allergies (feel tired or hyper-active after eating)

____ Clumsy

*____ Daydreams excessively

*____ Difficulty budgeting time

*____ Poor organizational skills

*____ Difficulty concentrating

*____ Difficulty focusing eyes

*____ Difficulty following directions

____ Letter/number reversal

*____ Lies

*____ Mood swings

*____ Over- or underactive

____ Poor eye-hand coordination

*____ Poor reading comprehension

____ Poor reading skills

____ Poor balance

*____ Poor spelling

*____ Difficulty telling time

____ Dizziness/vertigo/balance problems

____ Eye strain/rubs eyes a lot

*____ Fear of speaking in front of a group

*____ Trouble remembering directions

*____ Trouble remembering months of the year

*____ Trouble remembering names

____ Trouble remembering right/left

*____ Trouble remembering times tables

____ Trouble differentiating colors

____ Headaches

*____ Phobias/fears (explain) _____

_____

____ Speech difficulties (explain) _____

_____

____ Other (explain) _____

_____

*____ Poor arithmetic

*____ Rests head on arm while working

*____ Short attention span

*____ Slow in completing work

____ Stops in the middle of a game

____ Test or performance anxiety

*____ Timid/shy

____ Doesn't read for pleasure

*____ Impatient/restless/fidget

*____ Impulsive

____ Inappropriate drowsiness

*____ Lack confidence

*____ Procrastinate/projects incomplete

If you found yourself checking quite a few of the above characteristics, you may be feeling anxious and worried at this point. The good news is that help is available to correct these behaviors and more through the revolutionary developments in muscle testing and acupressure.

Appendix B

Research Supporting Clinical Observations

Note: The full text of these studies is available on-line at www. crossinology.com. A simplified version is presented here to make the results more accessible and understandable.

Steady State Visual Evoked Potential (SSVEP) Topography Changes

In 1995, when I was enrolled in an advanced-degree program in neuroscience at Swinburne University in Australia, I conducted a research project to investigate the effects of Brain Integration Technique on activity in the cortex—the place in the brain where we think and initiate learning and decision making. I also decided to measure the effects of brain integration on two areas often associated with learning difficulties: auditory short-term memory and reading comprehension.

Earlier in 1995, Silberstein et al. had used a newly developed, more sophisticated electroencephalogram (EEG), called the Steady State Visual Evoked Potential (SSVEP), to generate maps of cortical activity during learning and other cognitive processes. This approach was an ideal way to investigate the changes in brain activity associated with attention-oriented and decision-making tasks because the amplitude of the SSVEP could be estimated with just one to five seconds of recorded activity.

One male and four females, ranging in age from eighteen to forty-four, volunteered for the study. All of them had a history of learning difficulties. The SSVEP procedure involved attaching sixty-four electrodes to the scalp. The test was administered three times for each subject: once to familiarize him or her with the process and to eliminate any "novelty" effect, then as a pretreatment assessment of his or her SSVEP response, and finally as an assessment of changes in the brain after the BIT treatment.

The task that was tested was the ability to respond every time the letter A was followed by an X on a monitor screen. A series of random letters was shown on the screen, so the subjects needed to focus on watching for an A in anticipation that an X might follow. If the X did follow, the subjects had to decide to respond; if the X did not follow, the subjects had to decide not to respond. The subjects' decision-making responses were tested and recorded on an SSVEP image chart.

Prior to the BIT treatment, all subjects showed brain activity predominantly in their occipito-parietal lobes (located in the back of the head) where visual processing is performed, with little or no activity in their frontal lobes (behind the forehead), an area that has been shown to play a critical role at times of decision making[8]. People without learning difficulties have activity in their frontal lobes at the moment of making a decision, but prior to treatment, the subjects in this study did not. However, following the BIT treatment, all subjects showed considerably increased activation of

---

8   P. L. Nunez, *Neocortical Dynamics and Human EEG Rhythms*, Chapter 6 (New York: Oxford University Press, 1995).

the frontal lobes, as is normal. In fact, the lowest level of activity was now in the occipito-parietal lobes. The results, shown in the brain maps in Figure 1, clearly pointed to a change in brain activity resulting from the BIT treatment.

These results were interesting because they suggested that the BIT treatment had made physiological changes in brain activity (cortical activity) consistent with increased attention and decision-making capabilities. The patterns of cortical activity, as measured by SSVEP mapping, changed from patterns typical of ADD individuals to patterns normally seen in subjects without ADD performing similar tasks. The study showed that people with ADD simply cannot activate the brain areas involved in

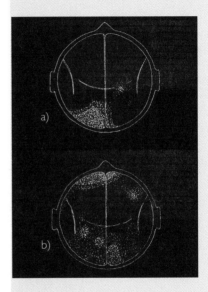

Figure1: Diagram shows view looking down on the brain from above.
The nose is at the top and light color shows activity.

a) no activity in frontal lobes when decision-making
b) same subject now showing frontal lobe activity when decision-making.

"paying attention" that are required for anticipating outcomes; the results suggest that BIT treatment helps people overcome ADD by opening up or activating those brain areas.

In addition to the SSVEP testing, I administered several standard psychometric tests to measure auditory short-term memory and reading comprehension. The test for auditory short-term memory involved digit-span recall—that is, the ability to recall a number of digits randomly presented forward and then backward. The test started with two digits and increased by one digit per trial until the subject could no longer recall the numbers in sequence. For example, I might have presented aloud a string of numbers such as 7, 5, 2, 6, 3, 8, 1 and asked the subjects to repeat those numbers in the same order presented, relying on auditory short-term memory (or an "audio playback") in their brains of what they had just heard. If they correctly repeated all seven numbers, their forward digit-span score would be a 7—about average for adults. After the BIT treatment, the scores of all the subjects increased from below 7 to 7 or above.

Next, they were asked to recall the numbers backward, from last to first (in the example above, they would say 1, 8, 3, etc.). The backward digit-span task is an important measure of visual memory. M. D. Lezak suggests that the reversing operation depends upon internal visual scanning.[9] In other words, this task relies on the brain's ability to make a mental picture of the numbers and then to "read" them in reverse. The average backward digit-span score for adults is 6. Before the BIT treatment, all the individuals in the study had backward digit-span scores that were marginal to borderline, at just 3 or 4 digits. After treatment, all subjects' backward digit-span scores rose to 6, or above, which is at or above the adult average (see Figure 2).

---

9   M. D. Lezak, *Neuropsychological Assessment*, 2nd ed. (New York: Oxford University Press, 1983).

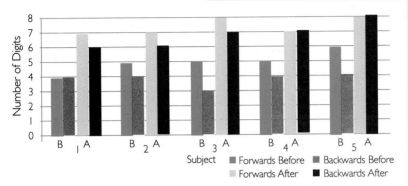

Figure 2: Forward and backward digit-span scores before and after acupressure treatment for learning difficulties. Each subject is shown individually, numbered from 1 to 5.

In regard to the BIT-treated individuals' increased ability to recall digits backward, it should be noted that Damasio has shown that working memory predominantly requires prefrontal activity (in the forehead region) and dorsolateral frontal activity (generally in the area behind the forehead).[10] The SSVEP scans showed increased activity in those regions following BIT treatment, suggesting that the subjects had significantly increased capacity in the areas of the brain responsible for working memory.

But perhaps the most compelling evidence of the changes that the BIT treatment made possible for the individuals in this study can be seen in their reading-comprehension scores. I gave each one the Neale Reading Comprehension Test, a widely used gauge that asks subjects to read a passage and then respond to eight questions about its content. Due to their learning difficulties, all of the subjects had poor reading comprehension prior to the BIT treatment.

10 A. R. Damasio, *Descartes' Error: Emotion, Reason and the Human Brain* (New York: Grosset/Putnam, 1994).

Adults without learning difficulties typically score at 90 percent or higher. In this study, the subjects' scores ranged from a high of 62.5 percent to a low of 0 percent; one person could not correctly answer a single question about the material just read. After the BIT treatment for learning difficulties, all subjects scored 100 percent on reading comprehension (see Figure 3). Since reading comprehension relies on an array of perceptual and cognitive functions, the results strongly suggest that the BIT treatment resulted in widespread improvement in perceptual and cognitive abilities.

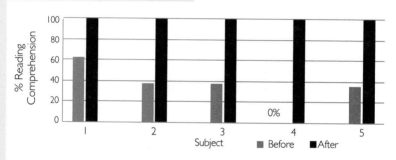

Figure 3: Percentage reading comprehension on Neale Reading Comprehension Test before and after acupressure treatment for learning difficulties.

The impact of these improvements at the clinical level became clear through interviews with the individuals after the acupressure treatment. Their comments were typical of what I have routinely encountered from clients:

- "I used to find the course I am studying very stressful and draining, especially before exams. The last exam was a breeze, and I walked into the exam room completely calm."

- "I have better comprehension and attention in both reading and listening."

- "Others remark on a complete change in me. I am now more focused and 'present' whereas I used to drift off."

Measuring BIT's Effects on Children with Learning Difficulties

Another study involved twenty school-age children from the Melbourne Applied Physiology Center in Australia, the institution I started in 1989. They ranged in age from six to nineteen years, and all had been referred to me because they had been diagnosed with learning difficulties. I divided them into two groups: one received the BIT acupressure treatment; the other received no treatment.

I tested their performance on one subtest of the WISC IIIR: Digit Span. I also administered the Inspection Time test and the Neale Reading Comprehension Test. The reason I decided to use a subtest of the standard intelligence test was not to measure intelligence but rather to assess performance in a cognitively demanding task. I tested all the subjects once and then retested them six to eight weeks later.

The visual Inspection Time (IT) test involves a simple, two-choice discrimination task. The test determines how long a subject takes to inspect and identify the correct stimulus—an object she is told to look for. The test, conducted on a computer monitor, displays an indefinite number of trials. Each correct answer reduces the time the subject is given to inspect the image and decide if it is the object she is seeking. Eventually, the length of time the image is displayed is so short that the subject will not be able to identify the correct image and will make a mistake. At this point, the individual receives a score. The smaller the number for IT, the faster she is able to process an image "flashed" in front of her, so low scores are desirable. The average for people without learning difficulties is less than 120 milliseconds.

Most of the subjects initially had much longer inspection times than the average for children without learning difficulties. In the group that did not receive BIT treatment, inspection times remained about the same or even increased from the first to the second round of testing. By contrast, results for the BIT-treatment group showed that all individuals improved their scores for visual information processing. Since IT testing has been highly correlated to performance or academic ability, these test results support the empirical observations that BIT treatment improves the ability to perform in school (see Figures 4a and 4b).

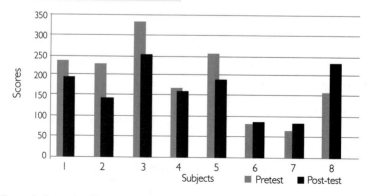

Figure 4a: Inspection Time scores for the nontreatment group at the pretest and post-test stages of the study. Low scores are desirable on this test.

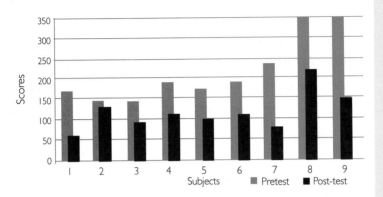

Figure 4b: Inspection Time scores for the treatment group at the pretest and post-test stages of the study. Low scores are desirable on this test.

The digit-span test scores were equally, if not more, dramatic. All but one of the children demonstrated a deficit age-specific digit span, meaning they were able to recall fewer digits (at least two less) than their peers without learning difficulties. Children who have a digit-span deficit consistently demonstrate difficulty with the memorization of facts and rote learning. They may learn a number of words or their multiplication tables one week but be unable to recall them the following week. When only the forward digit span improves but the backward digit span remains deficient, children often continue to have problems retaining spelling words and multiplication tables. However, when both forward and backward digit spans improve to within the normal range for their age, the subjects' ability to perform these tasks improves concomitantly.

Scores in the nontreatment group remained virtually unchanged between the first and second rounds of testing. The children who received BIT treatment, however, had significant increases in both forward and backward digit-span scores from pretreatment to post-treatment, with most gaining a two- to three-digit increase in the number of digits they could recall, forward and backward. Further, it should be noted that the increase in backward digit-span scores relative to the nontreatment group was especially significant. Again, the ability to recall digits backward relies on visual processing memory, strongly suggesting that this area of brain capacity was greatly enhanced by BIT treatment (see Figures 5a and 5b).

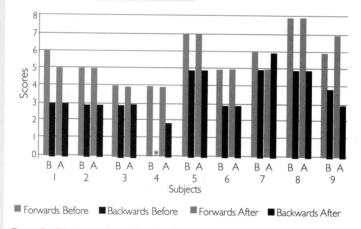

Figure 5a: Digit-span scores for the nontreatment group at the pretest (B) and post-test (A) stages of the study. (* Zero backwards score as Subject #4 could not understand the concept of reversing digits. B= before A=after.)

Finally, this study, like the one conducted with adults, held the most compelling evidence in the reading-comprehension scores. I administered the Neale Analysis of Reading Ability—Revised (1966), which asks subjects to read an age-appropriate passage and then respond to eight questions about the content. Again, average scores are in the 90 percent range for people without learning difficulties.

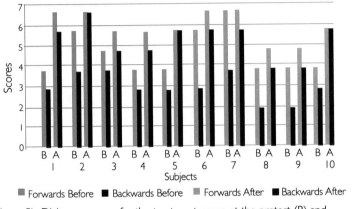

Figure 5b: Digit-span scores for the treatment group at the pretest (B) and post-test (A) stages of the study. (B= before A=after.)

Reading comprehension for the nontreatment group varied considerably between the two trials. For several children, comprehension decreased, whereas for others, it increased or remained the same. In the BIT treatment group, average reading comprehension started at a level even lower than that of the other group before treatment. One sixteen-year-old was unable to read at all, despite the weekly private tutoring he'd received for several years, and an eleven-year-old could only recognize a few small words. Following BIT treatment, all individuals were now reading with a comprehension of greater than 80 percent. Remarkably, the two children who had been unable to read before treatment were now reading with full comprehension at an early reading level. The sixteen-year-old continued private tutoring to realize steady growth; the eleven-year-old's improvement continued even without special remediation. Figures 6a and 6b illustrates these dramatic results.

Reading comprehension for the nontreatment group (Fig. 6a) varied considerably between the pre- and post-tests, with a number of subjects decreasing their percentage comprehension, others increasing slightly, and others remaining the same. One subject was unable to read and therefore received no score.

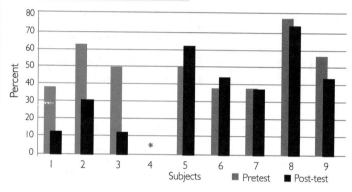

Figure 6a: Reading comprehension scores for the nontreatment group at the pretest and post-test stages of the study. (Subject #4 was a six-year-old who was unable to read.)

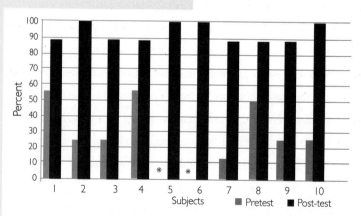

Figure 6b: Reading comprehension scores for the treatment group at the pretest and post-test stages of the study. (Subject #5 was an eleven-year-old who was unable to read. Subject #6 was a sixteen-year-old who was unable to read.)

Performance on these tests supported my empirical observations that acupressure treatment improves the individual's ability to perform two very different types of information processing. The type of fluid intelligence (that is, innate or inborn, as opposed to learned) measured with Inspection Time testing predominantly relies on the speed of processing visual information. Measures of fluid intelligence generally do not change significantly over time, as seen in the results for the nontreatment group. The results of the BIT treatment group demonstrated significant improvement in fluid intelligence within a remarkably short time frame.

My conclusions from these studies supported a new model of learning difficulties. This model is based on the disruption or loss of timing and synchronization of the neural activity in the diverse regions of the brain, both cortical and subcortical, which must be synchronized to produce normal learning ability. According to this model, learning difficulties arise from a lack of integration of functions that occur simultaneously in separate brain regions. In order to get a synchronous firing of neurons in many separate brain areas, focused activity at these different sites must be sustained long enough for a meaningful integration of disparate information and decisions to be made. As in the analogy of an orchestra, not only do the individual groups of instruments need to be playing the same piece at the same time, they also need to be synchronized and in tune with each other to produce a full, integrated, and harmonious sound.

Acronyms:

ADD - attention deficit disorder

ADHD - attention deficit/hyperactivity disorder

BIT - Brain Integration Technique

EEG - electroencephalogram

IQ - intelligence quotient

MRI - magnetic resonance imaging

PDD - Pervasive Developmental Disorder

SSVEP - Steady State Visual Evoked Potential

WAIS - Wechsler Adult Intelligence Scale

WISC IIIR - Wechsler Intelligence Scale for Children—Third Edition Revised

Recommended Reading

Demasio, Antonio R. *Descartes' Error: Emotion, Reason, and the Human Brain*. New York: Grosset/Putnam, 1994.

Gerber, Richard, M.D. *Vibrational Medicine*. Rochester, Vermont: Bear & Company Publisher, 2001.

Lyon, Michael R., M.D. *Is Your Child's Brain Starving?* Canada: Mind Publishing, 2002.

Quick Order Form

Fax orders: 1-303-449 0747.

E-mail orders: www.crossinology.com

Postal Orders: Learning Enhancement Center LLC

1705 14th Street, #313, Boulder CO 80302 USA

Please send _____book(s) at $18.95 each.

Name:_____

Address:_____

City:_____State_____Zip:_____

Telephone:_____

E-mail address:_____

Sales Tax: Please add $1.45 for each book shipped to Colorado.

Shipping by Air:

U.S. $4.00 for first book and $2.00 for each additional book.

International: $9.00 for first book and $3.00 for each additional book.

Payment: ❑ My check or money order for US$_____ is enclosed, payable to Learning Enhancement Center, LLC or please ❑ charge my VISA or Mastercard

Card number:_____

Name on card_____Exp.date_____

Signature: _____

Kris
Kea

Carole
Clam
Ann
Cindy

Kira
Juanita
Shelly
Tony